Contents

Formula Sheet

Exam 1

Exam 2

Answers

Published by Coordination Group Publications Ltd.

Contributors:

Charley Darbishire   Andy Park
Simon Little   Glenn Rogers
Iain Nash   Claire Thompson

ISBN: 1-84146-006-0

Groovy website: www.cgpbooks.co.uk

Printed by Elanders Hindson, Newcastle-upon-Tyne.

Occasional bits of clipart from CorelDRAW

GCSE Mathematics
Formulae Sheet: Higher Tier

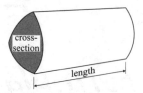

Volume of prism $=$ area of cross-section $\times$ length

Volume of sphere $= \frac{4}{3}\pi r^3$

Surface area of sphere $= 4\pi r^2$

Volume of cone $= \frac{1}{3}\pi r^2 h$

Curved surface area of cone $= \pi r l$

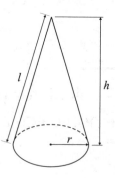

For any triangle ABC:

Sine rule: $\quad \dfrac{a}{\sin A} = \dfrac{b}{\sin B} = \dfrac{c}{\sin C}$

Cosine rule: $\quad a^2 = b^2 + c^2 - 2bc\cos A$

$$\cos A = \frac{b^2 + c^2 - a^2}{2bc}$$

Area of triangle $= \frac{1}{2}ab\sin C$

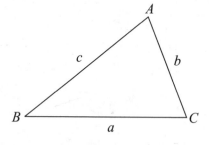

The quadratic equation:

The solutions of $ax^2 + bx + c = 0$, where $a \neq 0$, are given by:

$$x = \frac{-b \pm \sqrt{b^2 - 4ac}}{2a}$$

General Certificate of Secondary Education

GCSE
Mathematics
Paper 1A – calculator paper

Higher Tier

Time allowed: 2 hours.

Centre name				
Centre number				
Candidate number				

Surname	
Other names	
Candidate signature	

In addition to this paper you may need:
- A ruler.
- A protractor.
- A pair of compasses.
- An electronic calculator.
- Tracing paper may be used.

Instructions to candidates
- Write your name and other details in the spaces provided above.
- Answer **all** questions in the spaces provided.
- Do all rough work on the paper.
- Take the value of π to be 3.142, or use the π button on your calculator.

Information for candidates
- The marks available are given in brackets at the end of each question or part-question.
- You may get marks for method, even if your answer is incorrect.
- In calculations show clearly how you work out your answers.
- You are expected to use a calculator where appropriate.
- There are 20 questions in this paper. There are no blank pages.

Advice to candidates
- Work steadily through the paper.
- Don't spend too long on one question.
- If you have time at the end, go back and check your answers.

For examiner's use

Q	Attempt Nº			Q	Attempt Nº		
	1	2	3		1	2	3
1				12			
2				13			
3				14			
4				15			
5				16			
6				17			
7				18			
8				19			
9				20			
10							
11							
				Total 100			

1   Find, correct to 2 decimal places, the solutions of the equation

$$x^2 - 3x - 3 = 0$$

You must show your working. Do not use a trial and improvement method.

....

....

Answer _____

(3 marks)

2   Two rabbits are introduced to an uninhabited island. Within the first few months, they are breeding. This table shows the number of rabbits, r, occupying the island after t months.

Time (t) in months	0	1	2	3	4	5	6	7	8
Number of rabbits (r)	2	3	5	9	17	33	65	129	257

(a) Write down a formula for r in terms of t.

....

....

Answer (a) r = _____

(3 marks)

This graph shows the number of rabbits, r, inhabiting the island after t months.

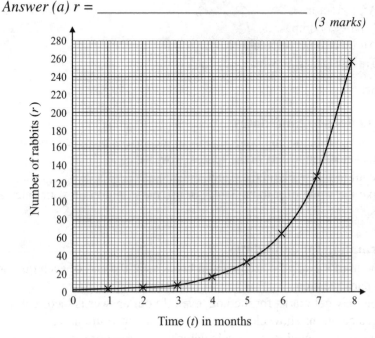

Time (t) in months

(b) (i) Find the gradient of the curve when $t = 6$.

....

....

Answer (b)(i) _____

(2 marks)

2   (b) (ii) What does the gradient represent?

*Answer (b)*_____

_____

(1 mark)

3   A travel agent has a sale on at the moment and has reduced all prices by 15%.
The reduced price of one particular holiday is £314.50.

What was the original selling price?

....

....

....

*Answer £*_____

(3 marks)

4   Boat A is 7.2 km from the lighthouse H on a bearing of 195°.
Boat B is 11.4 km from H on a bearing of 293°.

(Drawing not to scale.)

(a) Calculate the distance between boats A and B.

....

....

....

....

Answer (a) _____ km

(3 marks)

Question continued overleaf.

© 2001 CGP

4   (b) Calculate the bearing of boat A from boat B.

....

....

....

....

Answer (b) _____ °
(3 marks)

5   In the following diagram, *AB* is parallel to *CD*.
$AB = 5$ cm, $BE = 2$ cm, $CD = 8$ cm.

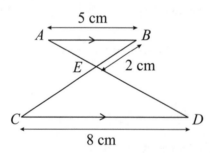

Using similar triangles, calculate the distance *CE*.

....

....

....

....

....

Answer _____ cm
(3 marks)

Leave blank

© 2001 CGP

6   In this diagram, $AB : AC = 3 : 4$.

(a)   Calculate the length AE.

....

Answer (a) _____ cm

(b)   Calculate the length DE.

....

Answer (b) _____ cm

(2 marks)

7   (a)   Write down a rational number between

(i)   7 and 8,

(ii)   0 and $\frac{1}{4}$,

(iii) $\sqrt{5}$ and $\sqrt{6}$.

....

....

....

Answer (a) (i) _____ (ii) _____ (iii) _____

(3 marks)

(b)   Write down an irrational number between

(i)   7 and 8,

(ii)   0 and $\frac{1}{4}$,

(iii) $\sqrt{5}$ and $\sqrt{6}$.

....

....

....

Answer (b) (i) _____ (ii) _____ (iii) _____

(3 marks)

© 2001 CGP

6

8   The diagram below shows a triangle S.

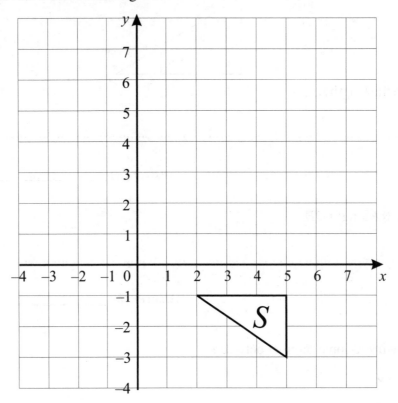

Three transformations are defined by:

R is a reflection in the line y = 1.

T is a translation with vector $\begin{pmatrix} -5 \\ -6 \end{pmatrix}$.

M is a rotation of 180° about the point (1, 2).

On the diagram draw and label:

(a)   R(S),

(1 mark)

(b)   TR(S),

(1 mark)

(c)   MTR(S).

(2 marks)

9   The scatter diagram below shows the masses of 15 hens and the masses of the eggs that they
     laid one day in the summer.

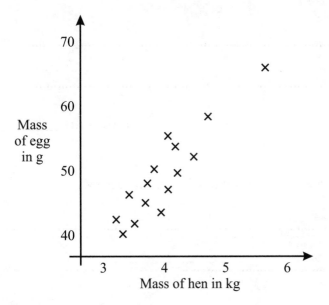

(a) Draw a line of best fit on the diagram.

(1 mark)

(b) Another hen, weighing 5 kg, also laid an egg that day.
     Use the diagram to estimate the mass of this hen's egg.
     Explain clearly how you got your answer.

     Answer (b) _____

     _____

     _____

     _____
                                                              (2 marks)

(c) You want to find an average value of the masses of the eggs in this sample.
     Which average — mean, median or mode — would best represent this data?
     Explain your choice.

     Answer (c) _____

     _____

     _____

     _____
                                                              (2 marks)

© 2001 CGP

8

10   (a)   Calculate $\dfrac{651.6 - 4.02}{7 - 8.2^2}$.

....

....

Answer (a) _____

(2 marks)

(b)   Using indices, write 392 as a product of its prime factors.

....

....

....

Answer (b) _____

(2 marks)

11   (a)   Find the value of a in the equation

$$3^a = \sqrt{27}$$

....

Answer (a) a = _____

(2 marks)

The cone in the diagram below has a volume of $81\,\text{cm}^3$.
The area of the base is $\sqrt{27}$ cm^2, and the height is 3^x cm.

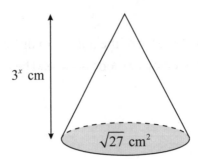

3^x cm

$\sqrt{27}$ cm^2

(b)   Calculate the value of x.

....

....

Answer (b) x = _____

(2 marks)

12 (a) Solve the equation

$$6(x + 2) = 2x - 6$$

....

....

....

....

Answer (a) x = _____

(3 marks)

(b) Solve the inequality

$$x^2 \geq 64$$

....

....

....

Answer (b) _____

(2 marks)

(c) Make *d* the subject of the formula

$$S = \frac{1}{2}xd^2 \qquad \frac{xd^2}{2}$$

....

....

....

Answer (c) d = _____

(3 marks)

© 2001 CGP

13   90 villagers take part in a sponsored run with a maximum of 50 laps.
      The number of laps completed by the villagers is recorded in the table below.

Number of laps	Middle of interval	Frequency	
1-5	3	2	
6-10		4	
11-15		5	
16-20		9	
21-25		7	
26-30		12	
31-35		8	
36-40		15	
41-45		3	
46-50		25	
		90	

(a) Complete the second column to show the middle of each interval.

(1 mark)

(b) Calculate an estimate of the mean number of laps.
     You may wish to use the last column of the table above.

....

....

....

                        *Answer (b)*_____

(4 marks)

14 A company makes coffee mugs.
    The total cost in pounds, *P*, of making *n* coffee mugs is given by

$$P = s + nt$$

where *s* and *t* are constants.
The cost of making 500 coffee mugs is £2250.
The cost of making 2000 coffee mugs is £4500.

(a) Calculate the values of *s* and *t*.

....

....

....

....

....

....

....

Answer (a) *s* = £_____

t = £_____

(4 marks)

The company can sell the coffee mugs for £3 each.
The company wants to make a profit.

(b) Calculate the minimum number of coffee mugs they must make and sell.

....

....

....

....

....

Answer (b) _____ mugs

(3 marks)

© 2001 CGP

15   Someone put £5000 in a bank account that paid interest at a rate of 7% per year. The interest
was added to the account at the end of each year.

(a) How much was in the account after 4 years, after the final interest payment had been added?

....

....

....

....

Answer (a) £_____
                                                        (3 marks)

(b) What annual rate of interest would be needed for a sum of money to double in 10 years?
Give your answer as a percentage to 1 decimal place. Show your working.

....

....

....

....

....

Answer (b) _____%
                                                        (4 marks)

16 Daffyd is using trial and improvement to find an answer to the equation

$$x^3 + x = 15$$

This table shows his first two tries.

x	x^3+x	Comment
2	10	*Too low*
3	30	*Too high*

Continue the table until you find a solution to the equation that's accurate to **1 decimal place**.

Answer _____

(4 marks)

17 Simplify the following expressions, writing your answers in the form x^k.

(a) $\dfrac{x^3}{x^7}$

....

Answer (a) _____

(1 mark)

(b) $\sqrt[3]{x^5}$

....

Answer (b) _____

(1 mark)

(c) $\sqrt{x^3 x^7}$

....

....

Answer (c) _____

(1 mark)

14

18 (a) Complete this table and hence draw the graph of

$$y = x^3 - 3x - 2$$

for values of x between -3 and 3.

x	-3	-2	-1	0	1	2	3
y	-20	-4					

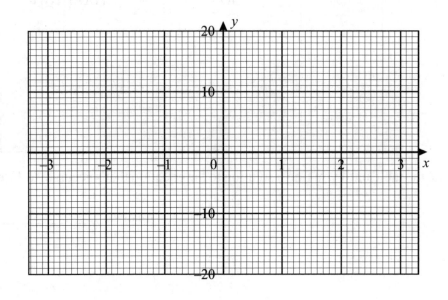

(2 marks)

(b) By drawing suitable straight lines on the graph, solve these equations:

(i) $x^3 - 3x - 2 = -10$

....

....

Answer (b) (i) x = _____

(2 marks)

(ii) $x^3 - 4x - 2 = 0$

....

....

Answer (b) (ii) x = _____

(2 marks)

Leav[e]
blan[k]

19   Fifty people enrol at an evening class. The table below gives information about how many men and women there were, and whether they were above or below the age of 30.

	Under 30	30 or over	**Total**
Men	13	11	24
Women	18	8	26
Total	31	19	50

(a)   One of the men is chosen at random.
      What is the probability that he is under 30?

....

....

Answer (a) _____
(1 mark)

(b)   One of the students under 30 is chosen at random.
      What is the probability that this student is female?

....

....

Answer (b) _____
(1 mark)

(c)   Two students are chosen at random.
      What is the probability that they are both male?

....

....

Answer (c) _____
(3 marks)

(d)   Two students are chosen at random from those students who are 30 or over.
      What is the probability that they are both female?

....

....

Answer (d) _____
(3 marks)

16

20   The diagram shows a cone.

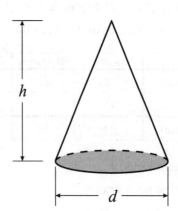

The diameter, d, of the bottom surface of the cone was measured as 72.2 cm, correct to 1 decimal place.

The volume, V, of the cone was found to be 0.33 m³ to the nearest 0.01 m³.

The formula for the height of a cone is:

$$h = \frac{12V}{\pi d^2}$$

Calculate the maximum possible height, h, of the cone. Give your answer in cm.

....

....

....

....

....

....

....

....

                                        Answer _____ cm

                                                                    (4 marks)

General Certificate of Secondary Education

GCSE
Mathematics
Paper 1B – non-calculator paper

Higher Tier

Time allowed: 2 hours.

Centre name				
Centre number				
Candidate number				

Surname	
Other names	
Candidate signature	

In addition to this paper you may need:
- A ruler.
- A protractor.
- A pair of compasses.
- Tracing paper may be used.

For examiner's use

Q	Attempt Nº			Q	Attempt Nº		
	1	2	3		1	2	3
1				12			
2				13			
3				14			
4				15			
5				16			
6				17			
7				18			
8							
9							
10							
11							
				Total 100			

Instructions to candidates
- Write your name and other details in the spaces provided above.
- Answer **all** questions in the spaces provided.
- Do all rough work on the paper.

Information for candidates
- The marks available are given in brackets at the end of each question or part-question.
- You may get marks for method, even if your answer is incorrect.
- In calculations show clearly how you work out your answers.
- There are 18 questions in this paper. There are no blank pages.

Advice to candidates
- Work steadily through the paper.
- Don't spend too long on one question.
- If you have time at the end, go back and check your answers.

18

1   (a) Work out

      (i) 16^0

Answer (a)(i) _____

(1 mark)

      (ii) $\dfrac{1}{3^{-2}}$

....

Answer (a)(ii) _____

(2 marks)

(b) Factorise completely $8x + 12x^2$.

....

....

Answer (b) _____

(2 marks)

(c) Solve $x^2 - x - 6 = 0$.

....

....

....

Answer (c) _____

(3 marks)

2   The mass, m, of a certain type of metal ball bearing is directly proportional to the cube of its
     diameter, d.
     When $d = 5\,\text{mm}$, $m = 2\,\text{g}$.

(a) Find a formula for m in terms of d.

     ....

     ....

     ....

                         Answer (a) m = _____
                                                              (3 marks)

(b) Calculate the diameter of a ball bearing of this kind whose mass is 16g.

     ....

     ....

     ....

                         Answer (b) d = _____
                                                              (2 marks)

3   (a) Express $x^2 - 6x + 7$ in the form $(x - a)^2 - b$, where a and b are numbers to be found.

     ....

     ....

     ....

                         Answer (a) _____
                                                              (2 marks)

(b) Hence, or otherwise, solve the equation $x^2 - 6x + 7 = 0$.

     ....

     ....

     ....

                         Answer (b) _____
                                                              (3 marks)

20

4 (a) Costas measures the height of his desk.
He says it is 85 cm tall, correct to the nearest centimetre.
What is the minimum possible height of the desk?

Answer (a) _____ cm

(b) Costas now measures his sister's height.
He says that she is 130 cm tall, correct to the nearest 2 cm.
What is his sister's maximum possible height?

Answer (b) _____ cm
(2 marks)

5 (a) Solve the equation $x^2 - 3x - 10 = 0$

....

....

Answer (a) _____
(2 marks)

(b) Solve the inequality $4(7x + 1) > 12x - 32$

....

....

Answer (b) _____
(3 marks)

(c) Write as a single fraction $\dfrac{3}{x-1} + \dfrac{4}{x}$

$\dfrac{3x + 4(x-1)}{x(x-1)}$ $\dfrac{1}{3} + \dfrac{1}{4}$

....

....

Answer (c) _____
(2 marks)

6   This is the graph of $y = x^2$.

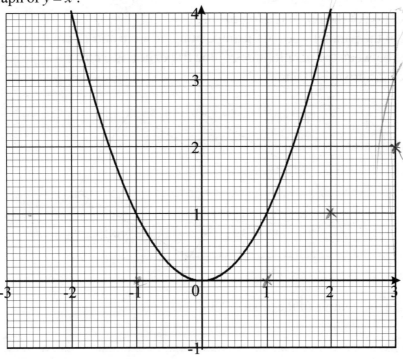

$y = x - 1$

(a) Use the graph to solve the inequality

$$2 \le x^2 \le 3.$$

....

....

....

....

Answer (a) _____

(3 marks)

(b) By drawing a straight line on the same grid, find both solutions of the equation

$$x^2 + x - 1 = 0.$$

....

....

....

Answer (b) x = _____ *and x =* _____

(3 marks)

22

7   The diagram below shows a prism.
     The cross-section of the prism is a trapezium.
     The lengths of the parallel sides of the trapezium are 4 cm and 12 cm.
     The distance between the parallel sides of the trapezium is 6 cm.
     The length of the prism is 10 cm.

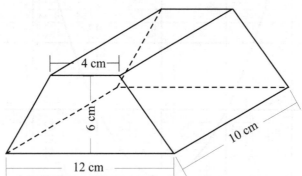

(a) Calculate the volume of the prism.

     ....

     ....

     ....

     ....

                                          Answer (a) _____ cm³
                                                              (3 marks)

     The prism is made out of silver.
     Silver has a density of 10.5 grams per cm³.

(b) Find the mass of the prism in kilograms.

     ....

     ....

     ....

     ....

                                          Answer (b) _____ kg
                                                              (2 marks)

8   This is part of the graph of $y = 7x - x^2$.

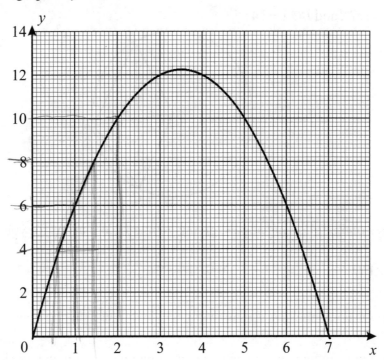

(a) Calculate an estimate of the gradient of the curve at the point $(1, 6)$.

....

....

....

....

Answer (a) _____

(3 marks)

(b) You are told that w is proportional to v-squared.
     Given that $w = 28$ when $v = 2$, find a formula for w in terms of v.

....

....

....

....

Answer (b)   w = _____

(3 marks)

24

9   In the diagram, the centre of the circle is at *O*.
     Angle *OAC* = 17°, and *BOA* = 74°.

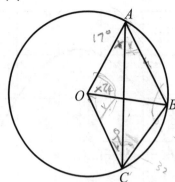

Find the sizes of the following angles, giving geometrical reasons for your answers.

(a) Angle *ACO*

....

....

Answer (a) _____°

(2 marks)

(b) Angle *COA*

....

....

Answer (b) _____°

(2 marks)

(c) Angle *CAB*

....

....

Answer (c) _____°

(2 marks)

(d) Angle *ABC*

....

....

Answer (d) _____°

(2 marks)

10   Marcus has an unfair coin.
      When he tosses it, the probability that it will land on heads is 0.4.
      He is going to toss it twice.
      Work out the probability that it will

(a)   land on heads twice,

....

....

....

....

....

                              Answer (a) _____
                                                           (2 marks)

(b)   land on heads exactly once.

....

....

....

....

....

                              Answer (b) _____
                                                           (3 marks)

© 2001 CGP

11   The diagram shows a rectangle of length $2x + 7$ and width $3x$.
      (All measurements are in cm.)

$3x$

$2x + 7$

The perimeter is P centimetres, and the area is A square centimetres.

(a) Write down an expression in its simplest form, in terms of x, for

   (i) P,

   ....

   ....

                                        Answer (a)(i) P = _____

   (ii) A.

   ....

   ....

                                        Answer (a)(ii) A = _____
                                                                    (3 marks)

The perimeter, P, is 34 cm.

(b) Calculate the value of A.

   ....

   ....

   ....

                                        Answer (b) _____ cm^2
                                                                    (3 marks)

12 (a) The times in seconds (to the nearest second) for 20 students to run 100 metres are
shown in the table below.

Time in seconds	15	16	17	18	19
Frequency	2	5	7	3	3

(i) Write down the median time.

Answer (a)(i) _____ seconds

(1 mark)

(ii) Calculate the range of times.

Answer (a)(ii) _____ seconds

(1 mark)

(b) The times taken for seven other boys to run 200 metres have a median of 31 seconds and
a range of 12 seconds.
Give a possible list of the seven times for the 200 metres.

Answer (b) _____

(2 marks)

13 Given that $u = 2 + \sqrt{5}$ and $v = 2 - \sqrt{5}$, simplify the following expressions.
State whether your answer is rational or irrational.

(a) $u + v$

....

Answer (a) _____

(1 mark)

(b) $u - v$

....

Answer (b) _____

(2 marks)

(c) uv

....

....

Answer (c) _____

(3 marks)

28

14   (a)   Rearrange the following formula to find x in terms of a, b and y.

Leave blank

$$y = \frac{a}{(x+b)^2}$$

....

....

....

Answer (a) $x = $ _____

(3 marks)

(b)   One of the graphs below shows $y = \dfrac{a}{(x+b)^2}$ for $x \geq 0$.

You can assume that a and b are positive.

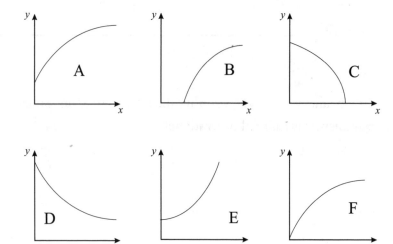

(i)   Write down the letter of the graph showing $y = \dfrac{a}{(x+b)^2}$.

Answer (b)(i) _____

(1 mark)

(ii)   Write down the coordinates of any points where the curve meets the axis.

....

Answer (b)(ii) _____

(1 mark)

15 The map below is drawn to a scale of 1 cm to 20 km. It shows an airport which is near the border of an unfriendly neighbouring country.

Leave blank

A plane can carry enough fuel to travel 120 km before it has to turn back to the airport. It is not allowed to go into the neighbouring country.

Shade on the diagram the area the plane could fly to and still have enough fuel to get back to the airport.

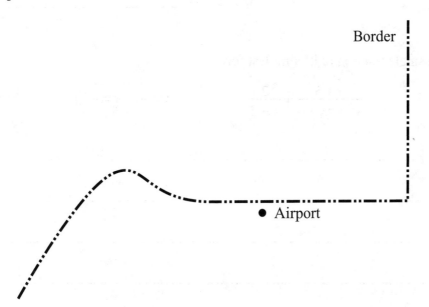

(4 marks)

30

16 (a) Factorise $x^2 + 5x + 6$.

....

....

Answer (a) _____

(2 marks)

(b) Write as a single fraction in its simplest form

$$\frac{x+5}{x^2+5x+6} + \frac{2}{x+3} \qquad (x \neq -2,\ x \neq -3)$$

....

....

....

....

....

....

....

....

Answer (b) _____

(4 marks)

14

© 2001 CGP

17 Frank has 12 ties in his tie drawer.

5 of the ties are red, and the other 7 are blue.

Frank takes 1 tie out of the drawer without looking. He records whether the tie is red or blue, and then puts it back in the drawer.

He then takes another tie out of the drawer, and records the colour again.

(a) Complete the tree diagram by filling in the probabilities.

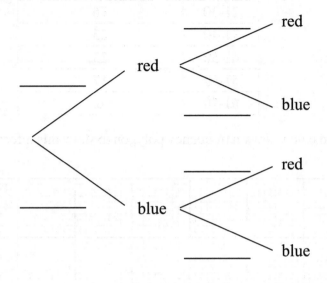

(2 marks)

(b) Calculate the probability that the two ties will be

(i) both blue,

....

Answer (b)(i) _____

(2 marks)

(ii) different colours.

....

....

Answer (b)(ii) _____

(3 marks)

18   A supermarket carried out a survey of the ages of its customers.
      The results are shown in the following table.

Leave blank

Age group (years)	Percentage of customers in this age group
1-10	2
11-20	11
21-30	16
31-40	25
41-50	23
51-60	17
61-70	6

(a) Using the grid below, draw a frequency polygon to show this information.

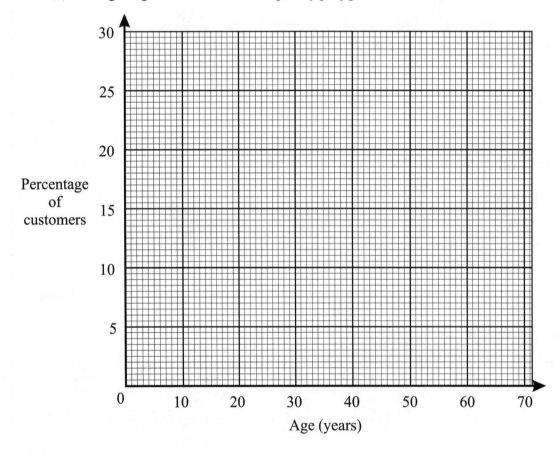

(2 marks)

(b) In which age group is the median age?

....

....

Answer (b) _____

(2 marks)

General Certificate of Secondary Education

GCSE
Mathematics
Paper 2A – calculator paper

Higher Tier

Centre name			
Centre number			
Candidate number			

Time allowed: 2 hours.

Surname	
Other names	
Candidate signature	

In addition to this paper you may need:
- A ruler.
- A protractor.
- A pair of compasses.
- An electronic calculator.
- Tracing paper may be used.

Instructions to candidates
- Write your name and other details in the spaces provided above.
- Answer **all** questions in the spaces provided.
- Do all rough work on the paper.
- Take the value of π to be 3.142, or use the π button on your calculator.

Information for candidates
- The marks available are given in brackets at the end of each question or part-question.
- You may get marks for method, even if your answer is incorrect.
- In calculations show clearly how you work out your answers.
- You are expected to use a calculator where appropriate.
- There are 20 questions in this paper. There are no blank pages.

Advice to candidates
- Work steadily through the paper.
- Don't spend too long on one question.
- If you have time at the end, go back and check your answers.

For examiner's use

Q	Attempt Nº			Q	Attempt Nº		
	1	2	3		1	2	3
1				12			
2				13			
3				14			
4				15			
5				16			
6				17			
7				18			
8				19			
9				20			
10							
11							
				Total 100			

1   The percentage increase in the cost of running a car after four years is given by

$$\left[\left(2-\frac{p}{20}\right)^4 - 3\right] \times 100 .$$

Calculate the percentage increase in the cost of running a car after four years when $p = 12$.

....

....

....

*Answer*_____%

(2 marks)

2   Carlos has just completed a 400 m race.

His finishing time, in seconds, is shown on the stopwatch.
Calculate his average speed in kilometres per hour.

....

....

....

*Answer*_____km/h

(3 marks)

3   Given that $p = 4 + \sqrt{5}$ and $q = 4 - \sqrt{5}$, simplify the following expressions.

Show all your working and state whether your answer is rational or irrational.

(a) $p + q$

....

....

*Answer (a)*_____

(1 mark)

(b) $p - q$

....

....

*Answer (b)*_____

(1 mark)

(c) pq

....

....

*Answer (c)*_____

(3 marks)

4   (a) Suzanne weighs a pot of yoghurt.
She says that the weight is 110 g correct to the nearest 10 g.
What is the minimum possible weight of the pot of yoghurt?

*Answer (a)*_____

(1 mark)

(b) Suzanne says that a slab of lard weighs 265 g to the nearest 5 g.
What is the maximum possible weight of the lard?

*Answer (b)*_____

(2 marks)

36

5   Here is a diagram of a company logo.

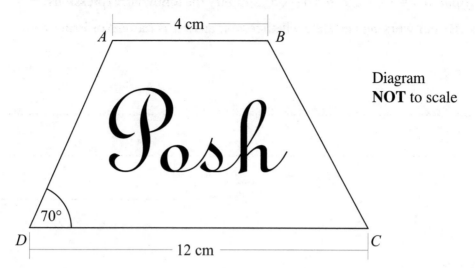

Leave blank

Diagram **NOT** to scale

The diagram is enlarged so that the length *AB* becomes 7 cm.

(a) Work out the length of the enlarged side *DC*.

....

....

Answer (a)_____cm

(2 marks)

The enlarged side *DA* is 14 cm.

(b) Work out the length *DA* on the original diagram.

....

....

Answer (b)_____cm

(2 marks)

(c) What is the size of the angle *ADC* in the enlarged diagram?

....

....

Answer (c)_____°

(1 mark)

4

© 2001 CGP

6   Factorise completely

$$ax - by + bx - ay$$

....

....

....

Answer _____

(2 marks)

7   The following formula gives acceleration, a, in terms of distance, s, and the speeds u and v.

$$a = \frac{v^2 - u^2}{2s}$$

(a) Find a when $s = 47$, $v = 28$ and $u = 42.5$.

....

....

....

....

Answer (a) _____

(1 mark)

(b) Rearrange the above formula to make u the subject.

....

....

....

....

Answer (b) _____

(2 marks)

8   A point moves around the outside of the isosceles triangle below. It is always 1 cm from the
      nearest point on the perimeter of the triangle.
      Construct the locus of the point.

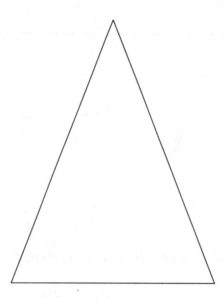

(3 marks)

9   Windermere is the biggest lake in the English Lake District. It covers an area of 1.6×10^7
      square metres. Lake Superior is the largest of the North American Great Lakes. It has a
      surface area of 8.21×10^{10} m².

      (a) What is the total area covered by these two lakes? Give your answer in standard form.
           (Assume that the figures given above are exact.)

      ....

      ....

                              Answer (a) _____m²
                                                                        (2 marks)

      (b) What is the ratio of the area of Windermere to the area of Lake Superior?
           Give your answer in the form 1 : *n*.

      ....

      ....

                              Answer (b) 1 : _____
                                                                        (2 marks)

10

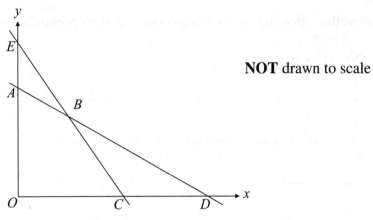

NOT drawn to scale

The quadrilateral $OABC$ is bounded by the lines $4x + 3y = 21$ and $3x + 4y = 21$, $x = 0$ and $y = 0$.

(a) (i) Write down the equation of the line AD.

....

....

Answer (a)(i)_____

(1 mark)

(ii) Find the coordinates of the points A and C.

....

....

....

....

Answer (a)(ii)_____

(2 marks)

(b) B is the point $(3, 3)$. Find the area of the quadrilateral $OABC$.

....

....

....

....

....

Answer (b)_____

(5 marks)

© 2001 CGP

40

11 (a) Express the following numbers as products of their prime factors.

      (i) 95

      ....

      ....

      ....

      ....

                               *Answer (a)(i)*_____
                                               (2 marks)

      (ii) 105

      ....

      ....

      ....

      ....

                               *Answer (a)(ii)*_____
                                                 (2 marks)

    (b) Two motorbikes go round a race track repeatedly. The first motorbike takes 1 minute 35
        seconds to complete a circuit and the other motorbike takes 1 minute 45 seconds.
        They start together on the starting line.
        Find the length of time, in minutes and seconds, before they are together again on the
        starting line.

    ....

    ....

    ....

                               *Answer (b)*_____
                                                  (3 marks)

© 2001 CGP

12 Use the method of trial and improvement to find the positive solution of

$$x^3 + x = 43$$

Give your answer to 1 decimal place.

....

....

....

....

Answer _____

(4 marks)

13 The diameter of a digestive biscuit is measured as 69.0 ± 1.5 mm.

The thickness of the biscuit is measured as 7.9 ± 0.5 mm.

Three hundred and seventy-six digestive biscuits are laid end-to-end in a straight line.

(a) Calculate the minimum length of the line of biscuits. Give your answer in metres.

....

....

....

....

Answer (a) _____

(3 marks)

(b) Calculate the maximum possible volume of one biscuit, in mm³.

....

....

....

....

Answer (b) _____

(3 marks)

14   A zebra at a zoo is sedated for a minor veterinary examination.
     The amount (in mg) of sedative remaining in the zebra's bloodstream after t minutes is given by the equation

$$y = 6 \times 4^{-\frac{t}{16}}.$$

(a) Write down the amount of sedative initially injected by the vet.

*Answer (a)*_____mg
(1 mark)

(b) Complete the following table of values. Give your answers to 2 decimal places.

Time after injection (t minutes)	5	10	15	20	25	30	35
Amount of sedative remaining (y mg)							0.29

(4 marks)

(c) Draw the graph of y against t.

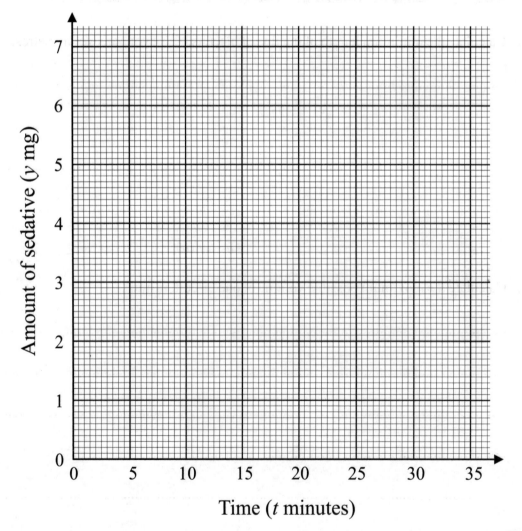

(3 marks)

15   Gemma, Taissa, Claire and Lindsay are the runners in a race.
      The probabilities of Gemma, Taissa, Claire or Lindsay winning the race are shown below.

Gemma	Taissa	Claire	Lindsay
0.19	0.26	0.23	0.32

(a) Calculate the probability that either Gemma or Lindsay will win the race.

....

*Answer (a)*_____

(1 mark)

Katherine and Angela play each other in a badminton match.
The probability of Katherine winning the badminton match is 0.54.

(b) Complete the probability tree diagram.

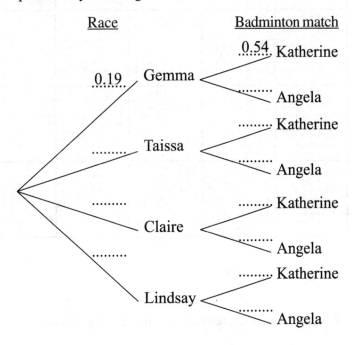

(2 marks)

(c) Calculate the probability that Taissa will win the race, and Angela will win the
     badminton match.

....

*Answer (c)*_____

(2 marks)

© 2001 CGP

44

16   The table shows information about the ages of the 100 members of a bowling club.

Age in years	Number of members
$15 \leq y < 20$	4
$20 \leq y < 25$	9
$25 \leq y < 30$	18
$30 \leq y < 40$	12
$40 \leq y < 50$	32
$50 \leq y < 70$	25

(a)   On the grid, draw a histogram to show this information.

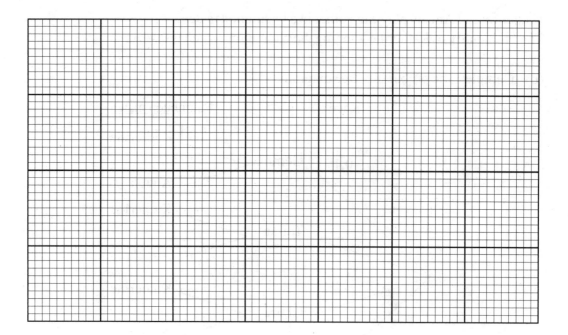

(4 marks)

The membership of the bowling club remains unchanged for 3 years

(b)   Calculate an estimate of the mean age of the members in 3 years' time.

....

....

....

....

*Answer (b)*_____ *years*

(4 marks)

© 2001 CGP

(c) How would a histogram of the ages of the same members in three years' time relate to the histogram drawn in part (a)? Assume that the same age ranges are plotted each time.

Answer (c) _____

_____

_____

_____

(2 marks)

17   Witherham has a population of 92 000 in an area of 118 square kilometres. To meet housing targets it needs to house an extra 14 000 people whilst increasing the area by only 7 square kilometres.

If this happens, by how much will the population density be increased?

....

....

....

....

....

....

Answer _____ people / square km

(4 marks)

46

18   (a) Express $x^2 - 6x - 5$ in the form $(x-a)^2 - b$, where a and b are numbers to be found.

....

....

....

*Answer (a)*_____

(2 marks)

(b) Hence, or otherwise, solve the equation $x^2 - 6x - 5 = 0$.

....

....

....

....

*Answer (b)*_____

(3 marks)

19   The lengths of 240 nails were measured to the nearest 0.1 mm.
The lengths were grouped according to the table below.

Length (mm)	Frequency	Cumulative Frequency
24.0 – 24.2	39	39
24.3 – 24.5	53	
24.6 – 24.8	76	
24.9 – 25.1	57	
25.2 – 25.4	15	

(a) Which is the modal group of lengths?

Answer (a) _____

(1 mark)

(b) Complete the table.

(1 mark)

(c) On the grid opposite, draw a cumulative frequency diagram to represent the distribution.

(3 marks)

Leave blank

© 2001 CGP

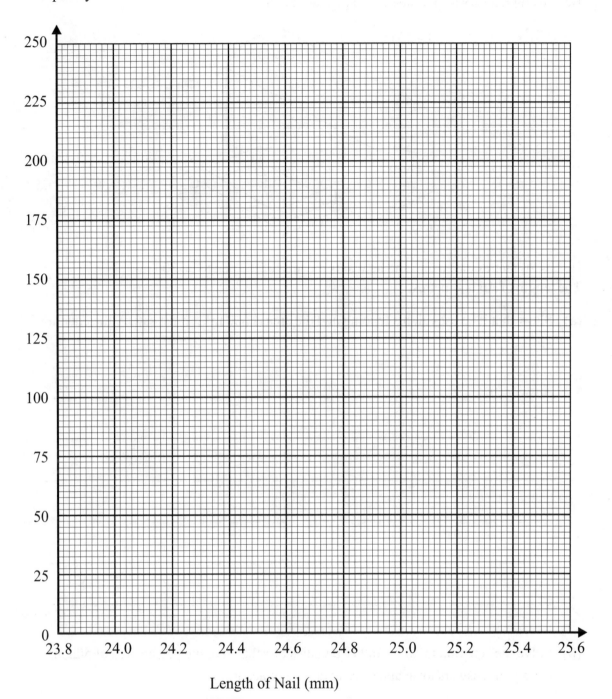

Cumulative Frequency

Length of Nail (mm)

(d) Describe how to use your graph to estimate the median value of the lengths of the nails. Write down your estimate.

Answer (d) _____

_____

_____

(2 marks)

20 A farmer wants to build a fence to make a rectangular pen.
    He is using his barn as one side of the pen, as shown.

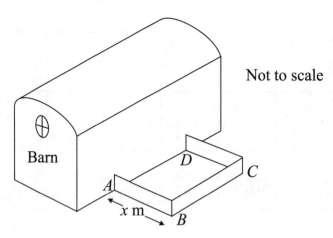

Not to scale

Barn

He has 80 metres of fencing and he wants the area of the pen to be 500 m².
The length of *AB* is *x* metres.

(a) Show that if he uses all his fencing and the area is 500 m², *x* must satisfy the equation

$$x^2 - 40x + 250 = 0.$$

Answer (a) _____

_____

_____

_____

_____

_____
                                                        (3 marks)

(b) Solve the equation in (a) to find **two** values of *x* that give the pen an area of 500 m².
     Give your answers to an appropriate degree of accuracy.

....

....

....

....

Answer (b) x = _____ m or *x =* _____ m
                                                        (3 marks)

General Certificate of Secondary Education

GCSE
Mathematics
Paper 2B – non-calculator paper

Higher Tier

Time allowed: 2 hours.

Centre name					
Centre number					
Candidate number					

Surname	
Other names	
Candidate signature	

In addition to this paper you may need:
- A ruler.
- A protractor.
- A pair of compasses.
- Tracing paper may be used.

Instructions to candidates
- Write your name and other details in the spaces provided above.
- Answer **all** questions in the spaces provided.
- Do all rough work on the paper.

Information for candidates
- The marks available are given in brackets at the end of each question or part-question.
- You may get marks for method, even if your answer is incorrect.
- In calculations show clearly how you work out your answers.
- There are 19 questions in this paper. There are no blank pages.

Advice to candidates
- Work steadily through the paper.
- Don't spend too long on one question.
- If you have time at the end, go back and check your answers.

For examiner's use							
Q	Attempt Nº			Q	Attempt Nº		
	1	2	3		1	2	3
1				12			
2				13			
3				14			
4				15			
5				16			
6				17			
7				18			
8				19			
9							
10							
11							
				Total 100			

1   Look at the following expressions. p and q are both lengths.

$$4p^2q \qquad 2p^3/q \qquad pq+5p \qquad p+q^3$$
$$p^3q^3/10 \qquad 2p(p+q) \qquad 5p + 4q \qquad pq^2$$

(a) Which of the above expressions could represent a perimeter?

Answer (a) _____

(1 mark)

(b) Which two of the above expressions could represent an area?

Answer (b) _____

(2 marks)

2   (a) Factorise $12a^2b - 8ab^2$

Answer (a) _____

(2 marks)

(b) Simplify

(i) $a \times a^6$

Answer (b)(i) _____

(1 mark)

(ii) $(3b^3)^2$

Answer (b)(ii) _____

(1 mark)

(iii) $\dfrac{b^2}{b^5}$

Answer (b)(iii) _____

(1 mark)

(c) Simplify

(i) $(3a^2)^{-2}$

....

Answer (c)(i) _____

(1 mark)

(ii) $8x^3y^2 \times \dfrac{3y^4}{4x^5}$

....

Answer (c)(ii) _____

(1 mark)

3   The times in a go-karting race are recorded to the nearest hundredth of a second.
     The fastest lap was achieved by Rolf Burton who completed a lap in 86.27 seconds.
     Give the upper and lower bounds of the possible times.

....

....

Answer   Upper Bound _____ *seconds*

Lower Bound _____ *seconds*

(2 marks)

4   (a) Rearrange the following equation to make *x* the subject.

$$y = 6x - ax$$

....

....

Answer (a) _____

(2 marks)

(b) (i)   Given that p > 1, write the following four terms in order of size, smallest first.

$$p^{-2}, p^{\frac{1}{2}}, p, \frac{1}{p}$$

....

....

*Answer (b)(i)*_____

(2 marks)

(ii) If 0 < p < 1, write down how the list above would be changed.

....

....

Answer (b) (ii) _____

(1 mark)

5 (a) (i) Give the next term in this number sequence.

1, 3, 7, 15, ...

Answer (a)(i) _____

(1 mark)

(ii) What is the rule for finding the next term of this sequence?

Answer (a)(ii) _____

_____

(1 mark)

(b) What is the nth term of the number sequence

$$\frac{1}{2}, \frac{1}{5}, \frac{1}{8}, \frac{1}{11}, \frac{1}{14}, ... \text{ ?}$$

....

Answer (b) _____

(2 marks)

6 Dr Venkman is conducting an experiment with a pack of cards. There are 4 different types of card, as shown below.

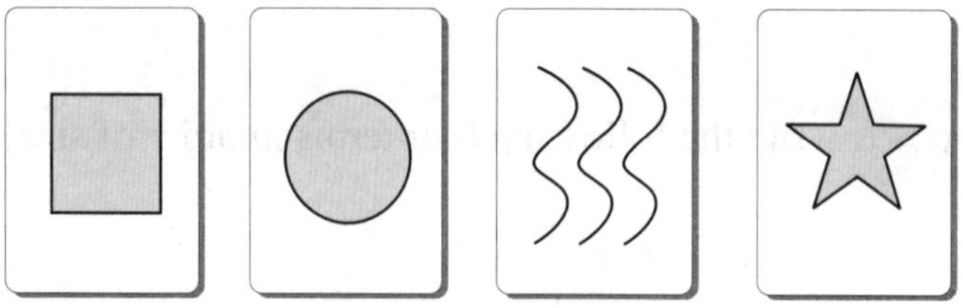

Dr Venkman selects a card from the pack without showing it to either of his 2 students, Leila and Paul. Both Leila and Paul then scribble down what card they think he has chosen. (Neither have any idea, so they just choose a card at random.)

On the first go, Dr Venkman picked a star.

(a) What is the probability that Leila got it right (i.e. drew a star)?

....

Answer (a) _____

(1 mark)

(b) What is the probability that both Leila and Paul got it right?

....

....

Answer (b) _____

(2 marks)

(c) What is the probability that Paul and Leila will draw different pictures?

....

....

....

Answer (c) _____

(3 marks)

7   Chris went for a walk, which is represented by the travel graph below.

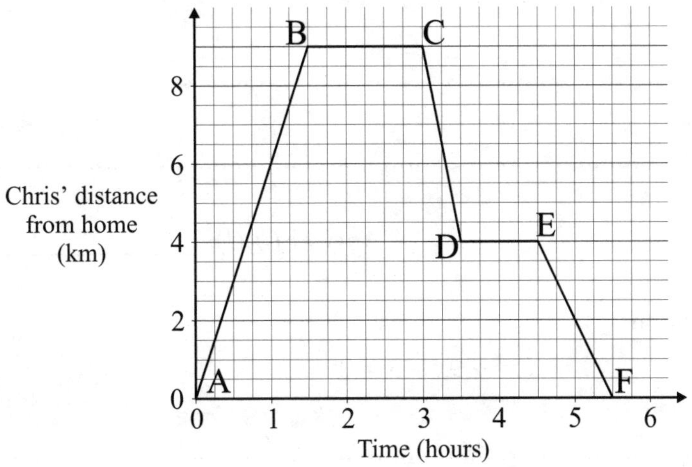

(a) Describe the part of the walk represented by the sections AB, BC, and CD.

Answer (a) _____

_____

_____

_____

(2 marks)

(b) In which section of the walk did Chris walk fastest?

Answer (b) _____

(1 mark)

(c) What was Chris' average speed for the first 3 hours?

....

....

Answer (c) _____ *km/h*

(2 marks)

54

8   (a)   Multiply out these brackets and simplify

$$(5x + 3)(2x - 4)$$

....

....

Answer (a) _____

(2 marks)

(b)   (i)   Factorise

$$2x^2 + 9x - 5$$

....

....

Answer (b)(i) _____

(1 mark)

(ii)   Solve the equation

$$2x^2 + 9x - 5 = 0$$

....

....

Answer (b)(ii) _____

(2 marks)

9   Solve the simultaneous equations

$$3x + 4y = 23 \qquad\qquad 2x - 2y = 6$$

....

....

....

....

Answer   x = _____

y = _____

(4 marks)

10   Below is a graph produced from a physics experiment.

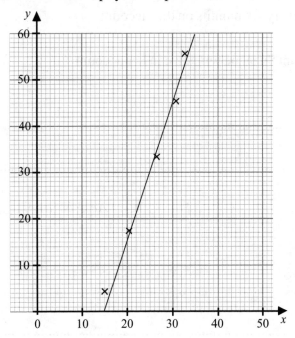

If the equation of the straight line is $y = ax + b$, find the values of a and b.

....

....

....

Answer a = _____ *b =* _____

(3 marks)

11   Solve the inequality

   $x^2 - 4x + 8 > (x - 4)^2$

....

....

....

Answer _____

(3 marks)

56

12   Suzanne has £500 in a very high interest savings account.
     10% interest is earned every six months on this account.

     Calculate the total amount Suzanne will have in her account
     (a) after 6 months.

     ....

     ....

                                      Answer (a) £ _____
                                                              (1 mark)

     (b) after 12 months.

     ....

     ....

                                      Answer (b) £ _____
                                                              (2 marks)

     (c) after 18 months.

     ....

     ....

                                      Answer (c) £ _____
                                                              (2 marks)

13   Find the area of the trapezium.

                                      Diagram **NOT**
                                      drawn accurately

     ....

     ....

                                      Answer _____
                                                              (3 marks)

© 2001 CGP

14   Four scatter graphs are shown below.

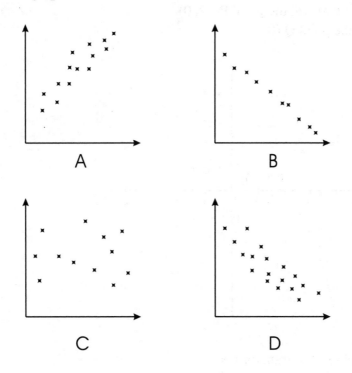

Which of the graphs A to D shows

   (a)   the strongest correlation?

                                        Answer (a) _____
                                                          (1 mark)

   (b)   a positive correlation?

                                        Answer (b) _____
                                                          (1 mark)

Which of the graphs A to D is most likely to be showing

   (c)   the results in a maths test and the heights of the candidates?

                                        Answer (c) _____
                                                          (1 mark)

   (d)   the ages of computers and their selling prices?

                                        Answer (d) _____
                                                          (1 mark)

15   Below is a sketch of the curve y = f(x).
The curve f(x) crosses the *x*-axis at the point P(–2, 0)
and crosses the *y*-axis at the point Q (0,1).

Leav
blan

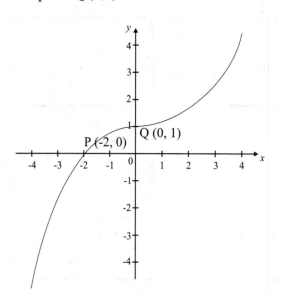

Sketch the following graphs of f(x) transformed.
For each transformed graph, state where the points P and Q have moved to.

(a)   y = f(x) + 3

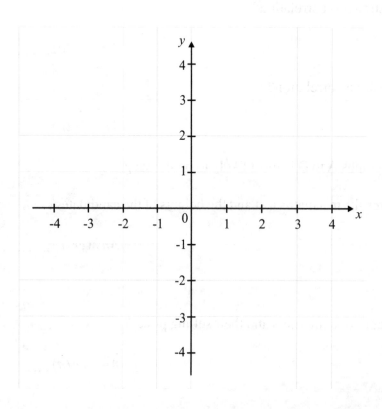

P has moved to (_____ , _____), Q has moved to (_____ , _____).

(3 marks)

(b) $y = 3f(x)$

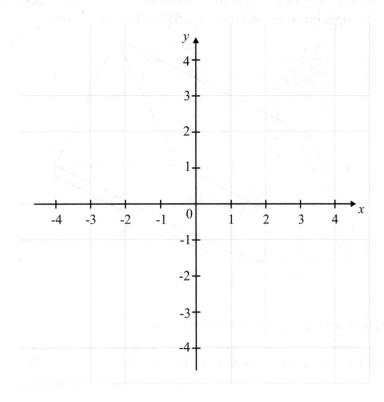

(3 marks)

P has moved to (_____ , _____), Q has moved to (_____ , _____).

(c) $y = f(x-2)$

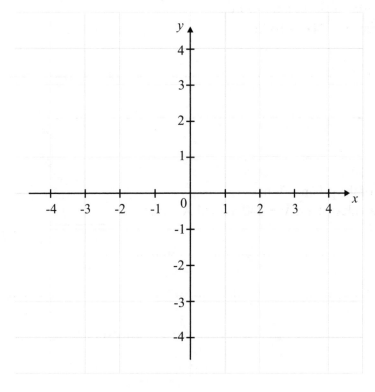

P has moved to (_____ , _____), Q has moved to (_____ , _____).

(3 marks)

11

60

16   The diagram below shows a prism whose cross-section is an isosceles triangle.
The isosceles triangle has sides of length $5x$, $5x$, and $6x$ (in metres).

Lea
blar

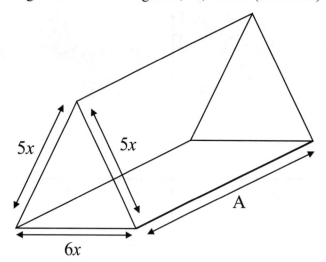

The total length of all the edges of the prism is E m.

(a)   Show that the length of the prism, A m, is given by $A = \frac{1}{3}(E - 32x)$.

Answer (a) _____

_____

(2 marks)

The surface area of the prism is S m².
(b)   Show that $S = 24x^2 + 16Ax$.

Answer (b) _____

_____

_____

(3 marks)

The volume of the prism is V m³
(c)   Find the value of x if V = 240 m³ and A = 5 m.

....

....

Answer (c) _____

(3 marks)

17   On the diagram below, PA and PB are tangents to the circle whose centre is O.

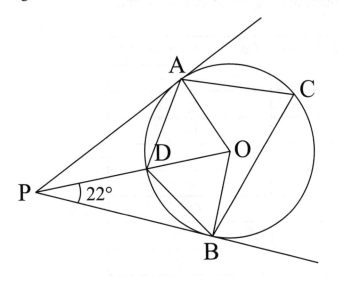

Diagram **NOT** drawn accurately

a)   State the size of angle *OPA*. Give a reason for your answer.

_____

_____

Answer (a) _____

(2 marks)

b)   Find the size of angle *POB*. Explain how you got your answer.

_____

_____

Answer (b) _____

(2 marks)

c)   Find the size of angle *BDP*. Explain how you got your answer.

_____

_____

Answer (c) _____

(2 marks)

d)   Find the size of angle *ACB*. Explain how you got your answer.

_____

_____

Answer (d) _____

(2 marks)

18   The life length of 160 light bulbs of a certain make was recorded.

Length of life (hours)	Cumulative Frequency
<10	2
<20	5
<30	11
<40	19
<50	34
<60	68
<70	117
<80	150
<90	158
<100	160

(a) Draw a cumulative frequency graph of the data below.

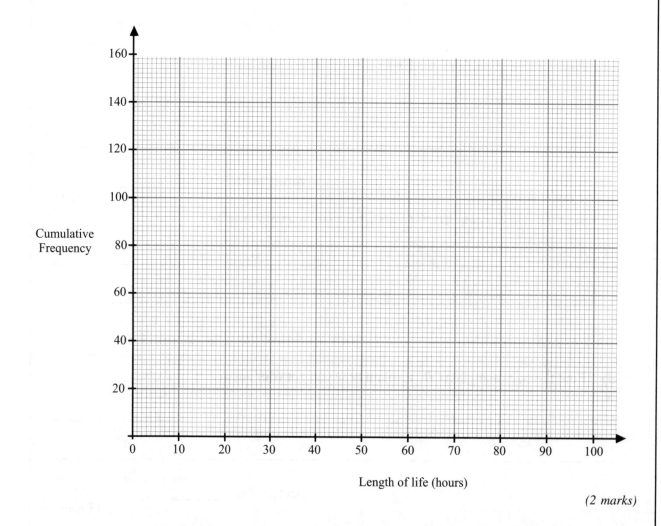

Length of life (hours)

(2 marks)

(b)   Estimate how many bulbs lasted more than 75 hours.

....

Answer (b) _____

(2 marks)

(c)   Using your graph, estimate:

   (i)   the median

....

Answer (c)(i) _____

(1 mark)

   (ii) the interquartile range

....

Answer (c)(ii) _____

(3 marks)

(d)   The median life length of a different type of bulb is 63 hours.
Its interquartile range is 24. Would you expect this bulb to be more or less reliable
than the other? Explain your reasoning briefly.

_____

_____

(1 mark)

64

19   ABCD is a parallelogram. $\overrightarrow{AD}$ = **a**, $\overrightarrow{DC}$ = **b**.

P is a point on AB such that $\overrightarrow{AP} = \frac{1}{2}\overrightarrow{AB}$. Q is a point on DB such that $\overrightarrow{DQ} = \frac{2}{3}\overrightarrow{DB}$

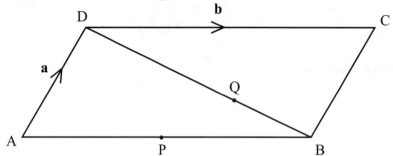

(a) Express the following vectors in terms of **a** and **b**:

(i) $\overrightarrow{PD}$

....

Answer (a)(i) _____

(1 mark)

(ii) $\overrightarrow{DQ}$

....

Answer (a)(ii) _____

(1 mark)

(b) Express the following vectors in terms of **a** and **b**:

(i) $\overrightarrow{PC}$

....

Answer (b)(i) _____

(1 mark)

(ii) $\overrightarrow{PQ}$

....

....

Answer (b)(ii) _____

(2 marks)

(c) What do your answers to parts (b)(i) and (b)(ii) tell you about the position of the point Q?

Answer (c) _____

_____

(2 marks)

Answers

Paper 1A

1 Use the quadratic formula with $a = 1$, $b = c = -3$.

$x = \frac{3 \pm \sqrt{(-3)^2 - 4 \times 1 \times (-3)}}{2 \times 1} = \frac{3 \pm \sqrt{21}}{2} = 3.79 \text{ or } -0.79.$

3 marks available — 1 mark for quoting the quadratic formula correctly, 1 mark for identifying a, b and c, and 1 mark for the final answer.
Learn THE QUADRATIC FORMULA and this question's a doddle.

2 (a) $r = 1 + 2$... 3 marks for the right answer, otherwise 1 for recognising it as an exponential function, and 1 for the correct working.

(b)(i)

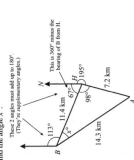

Gradient is found by drawing a tangent to the curve at the point ($t = 6$).

So gradient (approx.) $= \dfrac{\text{number of units up}}{\text{number of units across}} = \dfrac{153}{(8 - 4.55)}$
$= \dfrac{153}{3.45}$
$= 44.35 = \textbf{44.4}$

As this is judged by eye, allow any value from
$\frac{138}{3.7} = 37.3$ to $\frac{164}{3.3} = 49.7$.

2 marks: 1 for well-drawn tangent line, 1 for an answer between these limits.

(ii) The gradient literally represents *the rate of change of r with respect to t. Or the rate of increase in the number of rabbits per month at that moment in time.*
1 mark for an answer similar to the above.

3 Call the original selling price x. Then $0.85x = £314.5$. That means that $x = £314.5 \div 0.85 = £370$.
3 marks available — 1 for each of the ideas underlined, and 1 for the final answer.
Don't even begin to think you're finished with your revision unless you get these PERCENTAGES questions right every time.

4 (a) First draw the triangle below — you can work out the angle as the difference between the two ships' bearings from H.
$(= 293° - 195°)$.

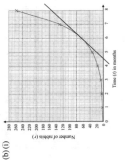

Then use the Cosine Rule to find the distance AB.

$AB^2 = BH^2 + AH^2 - 2(BH)(AH)\cos BHA = 11.4^2 + 7.2^2 - 2 \times 11.4 \times 7.2 \times \cos 98°$
$= 204.647 \Rightarrow AB = \sqrt{204.647} = \textbf{14.3 km}$

3 marks available — 1 for quoting the Cosine Rule correctly, 1 for inserting the correct figures (11.4 km, 7.2 km and 98°), and 1 for a correct final answer.

(b) Draw a diagram similar to that below, and then use the Sine Rule to find the angle $x°$.

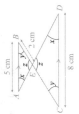

These 2 angles must add up to 180°. (They're supplementary angles.)

This is 360° minus the bearing of B from H.

The Sine Rule says $\frac{a}{\sin A} = \frac{b}{\sin B}$, so $\frac{14.3}{\sin 98°} = \frac{7.2}{\sin x°}$

$\Rightarrow \sin x° = \frac{7.2 \sin 98°}{14.3} = 0.499 \Rightarrow x° = \sin^{-1} 0.499 = 29.9°$ (to 1 d.p.)

So the bearing of boat A from boat B is $113° + 30° = \textbf{143°}$.
3 marks available — 1 mark for correctly quoting the Sine Rule, 1 for inserting the figures correctly, and 1 for a correct final answer.

5

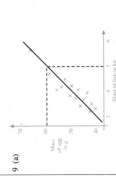

The two angles marked x must be the same (they are *alternate angles*). Similarly, the two angles marked y are the same, and so the two angles marked z must also be the same. So the triangles are similar, and the lengths of all the sides are increased by the same scale factor. This scale factor is $8 \div 5 = 1.6$. So increasing the length BE by a factor of 1.6 will give you the length of CE; this is $2 \times 1.6 = \textbf{3.2 cm}.$
3 marks available — 1 mark for explaining why the triangles must be similar, 1 mark for working out the correct scale factor, and 1 mark for the correct final answer.
Learn to love SIMILARITY — it's easy, and gets you loads of marks.

6 (a) Since the lengths AB and AC are in the ratio $3 : 4$, you know that the length BC must be 1/4 of AB, so the triangle ACE is an enlargement of triangle BCD with scale factor 4. That means that the lengths of all the sides of the smaller triangle must be multiplied by 4 to get the sides of the bigger triangle. So $AE = 4 \times BD = 4 \times 9 = \textbf{36 cm}.$
2 marks available — 1 for the correct scale factor, and 1 for the right answer.

(b) Also, the length CE must be $4 \times CD = 4 \times 12 = 48$ cm.
Therefore $DE = CE - CD = 48 - 12 = \textbf{36 cm}.$
2 marks for the correct answer. If your answer is wrong, get 1 mark for working out the length CE correctly.
Easy? No? Then do something about it and see RATIOS and ENLARGEMENT.

7 (a) There are millions of answers to these, so best to keep it simple. A rational number can be written as a fraction — an irrational one can't.
(i) One answer would be **7.5** (i.e. halfway between 7 and 8, which is $\frac{15}{2}$),
(ii) One answer would be $\frac{1}{4} \div 2 = \frac{1}{8}$ (halfway between again, and which you could write 0.125),

(iii) $\sqrt{5} = 2.236$ and $\sqrt{6} = 2.449$, so one answer would be **2.3** ($= \frac{23}{10}$).

(b) This time you need irrational answers — the simplest way to guarantee this is to throw in a square root sign.
(i) Now $7^2 = 49$, and $8^2 = 64$, so choose a number between 49 and 64, take the square root and there's an answer. So one answer would be $\sqrt{50}$.
(ii) Similarly, $0^2 = 0$, and $(1/4)^2 = 1/16$. So choose a number between these two and take the square root. One answer would be $\sqrt{\frac{1}{32}}$.
(iii) This time, choose a number between 5 and 6, and take the square root, e.g. $\sqrt{5.5} = \sqrt{\frac{55}{10}} = \sqrt{\frac{11}{2}}$.
One mark for each correct answer.
Just don't get it? Have a look at RATIONAL AND IRRATIONAL NUMBERS.

8

One mark for each of the triangles $R(S)$ and $TR(S)$ drawn correctly. Two marks available for $MTR(S)$ completely correct — still get one mark if the triangle has been rotated correctly but is in the wrong place.
Do these TRANSFORMATIONS questions carefully — that's my advice.

9 (a)

1 mark for a line close to that above, with about half the points to each side.

(b) Assume that the relationship between the mass of the hens and the mass of the eggs represented by the line of best fit is true for all hens between about 2 kg and 6 kg. If this is the case, then *a 5 kg hen can be expected to lay an egg weighing approximately 60 g.*
1 mark for justifying the use of the line of best fit, and 1 for the final answer.

(c) The mode is unsuitable, since no two eggs have the same mass. The mean would be heavily influenced by the exceptionally high value for one of the hens. *The median would be best.*
One mark for using the median, 1 for at least one reason to justify this. *STATISTICS — fascinating it ain't, but important it is.*

10(a) $\dfrac{651.6 - 4.02}{7 - 8.2^2} = \dfrac{646.58}{-60.24} = -10.75$.
Two marks if the final answer is correct, but 1 mark if the final answer is wrong but either the numerator or denominator in the fraction has been calculated correctly.

(b) $392 = 196 \times 2 = 98 \times 2 \times 2 = 49 \times 2 \times 2 \times 2 = 7 \times 7 \times 2 \times 2 \times 2$; so $392 = \mathbf{7^2 2^3}$.
1 mark for 7^2 and 1 mark for 2^3.
Want a hint? See NUMBERS and PRIME FACTORS.

11 (a) $\underline{27 = 3^3}$, so $\sqrt{27} = 27^{\frac{1}{2}} = (3^3)^{\frac{1}{2}} = 3^{\frac{3}{2}}$, i.e. $\mathbf{a = \frac{3}{2}}$.
2 marks for a correct final answer, but 1 mark if any of the underlined stages are given correctly.

(b) The volume of a cone is $\frac{1}{3} \times \text{area of base} \times \text{height}$. So the volume of this cone (in cm³) is $\frac{1}{3} \times \sqrt{27} \times 3^x = 3^{-1} \times 3^{\frac{3}{2}} \times 3^x = 3^{x+\frac{1}{2}}$, using the result from (a). This equals 81 (=3⁴). Therefore $x + \frac{1}{2} = 4$, or $\mathbf{x = 3\frac{1}{2} = \frac{7}{2}}$.
3 marks available — 1 mark for quoting the volume of a cone correctly, 1 mark for writing either $\frac{1}{3}$ or $\sqrt{27}$ correctly as a power of 3, and 1 mark for a correct final answer.
Finding it a bit hard-going? Take a look at INDICES.

12 (a) $6(x + 2) = 2x - 6$, and so $6x + 12 = 2x - 6$. Subtract $2x$ and then 12 from both sides to get $4x = -18$, or $\mathbf{x = -9/2}$.
1 mark for working out the brackets correctly, 1 for subtracting either $2x$ or 12 correctly from both sides, and 1 for a correct final answer.

(b) If $x^2 \geq 64$, then $\mathbf{x \leq -8 \text{ or } x \geq 8}$.
2 marks available — 1 for $x \leq -8$ and 1 for $x \geq 8$.

(c) $S = \frac{1}{2}xd^2$, and so $\underline{xd^2 = 2S}$. This means $d^2 = \underline{\frac{2S}{x}}$, and so $\mathbf{d = \sqrt{\frac{2S}{x}}}$.
3 marks for a correct final answer, or 1 for each underlined intermediate stage if you get it wrong.
If you want a hand, check out the ALGEBRA section.

13 (a)

Number of laps	Middle of interval	Frequency	Middle of interval × frequency
1-5	3	2	6
6-10	8	4	32
11-15	13	5	65
16-20	18	9	162
21-25	23	7	161
26-30	28	12	336
31-35	33	8	264
36-40	38	15	570
41-45	43	3	129
46-50	48	25	1200
		90	2925

1 easy mark for getting it right.
If you got this wrong, STAND ON YOUR HEAD AND COUNT TO 500.

(b) mean $= \dfrac{\text{total number of laps run}}{\text{total number of people}} = \dfrac{2925}{90} = 32\frac{1}{2} = \mathbf{32.5}$
4 marks for the correct answer, otherwise 1 mark for labelling the last column in the table correctly, 1 for filling it in correctly, and 1 for a valid method.
Just a hunch, but GROUPED FREQUENCY TABLES might be quite useful here.

14 (a) Substitute the values of n and P into the equation to find 2 simultaneous equations in s and t. These are $\underline{2250 = s + 500t}$, and $\underline{4500 = s + 2000t}$. Subtract the first from the second to get $2250 = 1500t$, which tells you that $\mathbf{t = 1.5}$. Then put this value of t back into one of the original equations to find $\mathbf{s = 1500}$.
4 marks available — 1 for each of the underlined equations written correctly, and 1 for each of s and t correct.

(b) The cost (in pounds) of producing n mugs is $1500 + 1.5n$. These can be sold for £3n. The company wants the selling cost to be greater than the production costs, i.e. $\underline{3n > 1500 + 1.5n}$. Subtract $1.5n$ from both sides to get $1.5n > 1500$, or $n > 1000$. So they must make and sell at least ***1001 mugs***.
3 marks available — 1 for saying that the selling costs are £3n, 1 for the underlined inequality, and 1 for the final answer (saying 1000 mugs is okay).
I used to hate questions like this too — but then I got my ALGEBRA learnt.

15 (a) At the end of the nth year, there is
$A\left(1+\frac{r}{100}\right)^n = £5000 \times \left(1+\frac{7}{100}\right)^n = £5000 \times 1.07^n$ in the account. So putting $n = 4$ gives ***£6553.98***.
3 marks available — 1 for quoting the compound interest formula correctly; 1 for putting in the correct values for A, r and n; and 1 for the right answer.

(b) If you start with £A, after 10 years this has to equal £2A. So you need to find r so that, $2A = A\left(1+\frac{r}{100}\right)^{10}$, i.e. find r so that $\underline{2 = \left(1+\frac{r}{100}\right)^{10}}$.
Now take the 10th root of both sides to get
$\left(1+\frac{r}{100}\right) = \sqrt[10]{2} = 1.0718$, which means that $\mathbf{r = 7.2\%}$.
4 marks available — 1 mark for putting n = 10 in the compound interest formula, 1 for producing the underlined equation, 1 for taking the 10th root of both sides, and 1 for a correct final answer. (You don't lose any marks for the wrong number of decimal places.)
COMPOUND GROWTH AND DECAY — Marvellous...

16 One possible table would be:

x	x^3+x	Comment
2	10	Too low
3	30	Too high
2.5	18.125	Too high
2.3	14.467	Too low
2.4	16.224	Too high
2.35	15.33	Too high

So the answer to 1 decimal place is $\mathbf{x = 2.3}$.
4 marks available — 1 mark for trying a value of x between 2.1 and 2.5 first, 1 mark for working out at least 2 values of $x^3 + x$ correctly, 1 mark for at least two correct reactions to a value of $x^3 + x$ that's too high or too low, and 1 mark for the correct final answer.
This sort of stuff's in the TRIAL AND IMPROVEMENT section.

17 (a) $\frac{x^3}{x^7} = x^3 \div x^7 = x^{3-7} = \mathbf{x^{-4}}$ — 1 mark.
(b) $\sqrt[3]{x^5} = (x^5)^{\frac{1}{3}} = \mathbf{x^{\frac{5}{3}}}$ — 1 mark.
(c) $\sqrt{x^3x^7} = \sqrt{x^{10}} = (x^{10})^{\frac{1}{2}} = \mathbf{x^5}$ — 1 mark.
If you got anything less than 3 marks, see INDICES as a matter of urgency.

18 (a)

x	−3	−2	−1	0	1	2	3
y	−20	−4	0	−2	−4	0	16

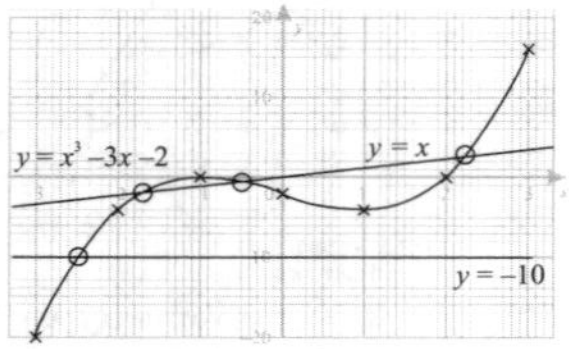

2 marks available — 1 for at least 4 correct entries in the table, and 1 for at least 4 points plotted correctly on the graph.

(b) (i) Draw the line $y = -10$. This will cross the first line when $x^3 - 3x - 2 = -10$, i.e. when ***x is approximately −2.5***.
2 marks available — 1 for drawing the correct line, and 1 for a value for x between −2.7 and −2.3.

(ii) Draw the line $y = x$. Then $x^3 - 4x - 2 = 0$ when $x^3 - 3x - 2 = x$, ie when the line $y = x$ crosses the line $y = x^3 - 3x - 2$. This happens when x is ***approximately −1.5***, ***approximately −0.5*** and ***approximately 2.2***.
2 marks available — 1 for drawing the correct line, and 1 for values for x between −1.7 and −1.3, between −0.7 and −0.3 and between 2.0 and 2.4.
Check out SOLVING EQUATIONS USING GRAPHS — if you need a hand, that is...

19 (a) There are 24 men in total, and 13 of these are under 30. So the required probability is $\mathbf{\frac{13}{24} = 0.542}$.
1 mark for a correct answer. (Give your answer as a fraction or a decimal.)

(b) There are 31 students under 30, and 18 of these are female. So the required probability is $\mathbf{\frac{18}{31} = 0.581}$.
1 mark for a correct answer. (Give your answer as a fraction or a decimal.)

(c) The probability that the first student is male is $\frac{24}{50}$, and the probability that the second student is also male is $\frac{23}{49}$. Therefore the probability that both students are male is $\frac{24}{50} \times \frac{23}{49} = \frac{552}{2450} = \mathbf{\frac{276}{1225} = 0.225}$.
3 marks available — 1 for the probability of the first student being male, 1 for the probability of the second student being male, and 1 for multiplying these answers together. (If one of the probabilitites is incorrect but the multiplication is done correctly, then get the mark.)

(d) There are 19 students who are 30 or over, and 8 of these are female. So the probability that the first student is female is $\frac{8}{19}$, and the probability that the second student is also female is $\frac{7}{18}$. Therefore the probability that both students are female is $\frac{8}{19} \times \frac{7}{18} = \frac{56}{342} = \mathbf{\frac{28}{171} = 0.164}$.
3 marks available — 1 for the probability of the first student being female, 1 for the probability of the second student being female, and 1 for multiplying the answers together correctly. (If one of the probabilitites is incorrect but the multiplication is done correctly, then get the mark.)
PROBABILITY — I know what you're thinking, but you really need to know it...

20 The maximum possible height, h_{max}, is given by $h_{max} = \frac{12V_{max}}{\pi d^2_{min}}$, where V_{max} and d_{min} are the maximum possible value of V and minimum possible value of d. If $V = 0.33$ m³ to the nearest 0.01 m³, then $V_{max} = 0.335$ m³. Similarly, if d is 72.2 cm to 1 decimal place, then the smallest d could be is 72.15 cm. So converting all units into metres, and putting these into the formula for h_{max}, you find that

$h_{max} = \dfrac{12 \times 0.335}{\pi \times (0.7215)^2} = \mathbf{2.458\ m,\ or\ 245.8\ cm}$.

4 marks available — 1 for stating the highest possible value of V, 1 for stating the lowest possible value of d, 1 for converting all measurements into the same units correctly (either metres or centimetres) and 1 for the correct final answer (in centimetres).
See APPROXIMATION if you get anything less than the full monty here.

Paper 1B

1 (a) (i) ***1***. (Anything to the power 0 is 1.) — 1 mark for the correct answer.
(ii) $\frac{1}{3^{-2}} = 3^2 = \mathbf{9}$. 2 marks for the correct answer. Only 1 mark for $\frac{1}{9}$ or 3.
(b) $\mathbf{4x(2 + 3x)}$ 1 mark for $4x$, and 1 mark for $(2 + 3x)$.
(c) $x^2 - x - 6 = (x - 3)(x + 2)$. So the solutions are $\mathbf{x = 3, x = -2}$.
3 marks for the correct answer, otherwise 2 marks for factorising the expression correctly (or 1 mark if your factors only give 2 of the 3 terms correct). (You still get the marks for using another method — e.g. the quadratic formula — as long as you get the right answer.)
There you go — another bog-standard ALGEBRA question.

2 (a) m is directly proportional to the cube of d, i.e. $\underline{m \propto d^3}$. This means that $\underline{m = kd^3}$, where k is a constant. Substitute the values $d = 5$ and $m = 2$ to find that $2 = 125k$, or $k = 2 / 125$. Therefore $\mathbf{m = \frac{2}{125}d^3}$.
3 marks for the correct equation, otherwise 1 for either of the 2 underlined expressions, and 1 for correctly substituting the values of d and m into whatever equation you get.

(b) You know the mass and need to work out the diameter, so rearrange the formula to find $d^3 = \frac{125m}{2}$, or $d = \sqrt[3]{\frac{125m}{2}}$. Now substitute the value $m = 16$, to find that $d = \sqrt[3]{1000} = \mathbf{10\ mm}$. Give yourself 2 marks for the correct answer, otherwise 1 for correctly rearranging the formula, or 1 for a correct solution of an incorrect formula (if you got part (a) wrong).
DIRECT PROPORTION — a laugh a minute.

3 (a) $x^2 - 6x + 7 = (x - 3)^2 - b$ (by making sure the number of x's is the same). Now compare these two expressions and you find that $b = 2$,
i.e. $x^2 - 6x + 7 = \mathbf{(x - 3)^2 - 2}$. (This is called 'completing the square'.)
2 marks available — 1 for '$(x + 3)^2$' and 1 for '−2'. (Get the marks if you say $a = 3$ and $b = 2$.)

(b) $x^2 - 6x + 7 = 0$ means that $(x - 3)^2 - 2 = 0$, i.e. $x - 3 = \pm\sqrt{2}$, or $x = 3 \pm \sqrt{2}$. Therefore $\mathbf{x = 3 + \sqrt{2}}$ *or* $\mathbf{x = 3 - \sqrt{2}}$
(or: $x = 4.41$ *or* $x = 1.58$)
3 marks for the correct answer, otherwise 1 mark for using a suitable method (you could use the quadratic formula here as well), and 1 mark for each correct solution (written as a decimal or a surd).
Struggling? Practise solving QUADRATIC EQUATIONS then.

4 (a) The minimum possible height is ***84.5cm*** — 1 mark available.
(b) The maximum possible height is ***131cm*** (or 130.99 recurring, which is equivalent). Anything less than this is wrong, as there would always be a larger number that would still be rounded down (even though 131 would be rounded up, not down) — give yourself 2 marks for the correct answer, but only 1 for 130.5 cm (if you didn't notice it was 2 cm divisions).
ROUNDING OFF VALUES — come on, it's a doddle if you bother to learn it.

5 (a) $x^2 - 3x - 10 = 0$ means $(x - 5)(x + 2) = 0$, so $\mathbf{x = 5}$ or $\mathbf{x = -2}$.
2 marks available — 1 for each correct answer (but no marks if any extra answers are given).
(b) $4(7x + 1) > 12x - 32$ means that $\underline{28x + 4 > 12x - 32}$, or $\underline{16x > -36}$, i.e. $\mathbf{x > -\frac{9}{4}}$.
3 marks for the correct answer, otherwise 1 mark for each of the underlined bits.

(c) $\dfrac{3}{x-1} + \dfrac{4}{x} = \dfrac{3x+4(x-1)}{x(x-1)} = \dfrac{7x-4}{x(x-1)}$. 2 marks for the correct answer, otherwise 1 mark for identifying $x(x-1)$ as the denominator.

6 (a) You can see that when $1.4 \le x \le 1.7$ or $-1.7 \le x \le -1.4$, the graph of $y = x^2$ is between 2 and 3. 3 marks for both ranges correct, or any set of answers that are identical to within 1 decimal place. It doesn't matter if '$<$' is used instead of '$\le$'. Lose a mark if the equality signs are the wrong way round, and lose a mark if any figures are nearly right (within 0.1), but not quite. No marks for anything 0.2 out or more.

(b) Draw the line $y = 1 - x$. Then this crosses the graph of $y = x^2$ when $x^2 = 1 - x$, i.e. when $x^2 + x - 1 = 0$. This is when $x = -1.6$ **and** $x = 0.6$. 3 marks for the correct answer, otherwise 2 marks for drawing the correct line, or 1 mark for drawing the wrong line but accurately reading the points of intersection. Also lose a mark if either or both of the answers aren't accurate to 1 decimal place.
If you can't see why, you need more practice SOLVING EQ'S USING GRAPHS.

7 (a) The area of a trapezium is (average of parallel sides) × (distance between them). So the area of this prism is
$\left(\dfrac{12+4}{2}\right) \times 6 = 8 \times 6 = 48\ cm^2$. The volume of a prism is (cross-sectional area) × (length), so multiply 48 by 10 and you find that the volume of the prism is **480 cm³**.
3 marks for the correct answer, otherwise 1 mark for substituting into either of the two underlined formulas correctly (2 marks for both) and 1 mark for the correct cross-sectional area.

(b) Density = mass / volume, so if the density of silver is 10.5 grams per cm³, then the mass must be $10.5 \times 480 = 5040$ grams (mass = density × volume), which is 5.04 kg.
2 marks for the correct answer, otherwise 1 mark for either of the two underlined formulas.
If you're thoroughly hacked off with this, go and relearn AREAS and VOLUMES.

8 (a)

gradient approx. 10 ÷ 2 = **5**

(b) w is proportional to v squared (i.e. $w \propto v^2$), so you can say $w = kv^2$, where k is just a number. Now substitute in $w = 28$ and $v = 2$, and you get $28 = 4k$, which tells you that $k = 7$. So **$w = 7v^2$**. 3 marks for the correct answer, otherwise 1 mark for either of the underlined formulas, and 1 mark for substituting the values of v and w into a formula correctly (even if it's the wrong one).

9 (a) Angle ACO must be **17°**, since the triangle OAC is an isosceles triangle. (Both OA and OC must be the same length, as they are both radiuses of the circle.) 2 marks for the right answer, otherwise 1 for spotting that it's an isosceles.

(b) Angle COA must be $180° - (2 \times 17°) = 146°$, since there are 180° in triangle OAC, and we know that two of the angles are 17°.
2 marks for the right answer, otherwise 1 mark for working it out using $180° - 17° -$ angle ACO (even if this bit was wrong in part (a)).

(c) The angles OBA and OAB are the same (since triangle OBA is isosceles) and must both equal $\frac{1}{2}(180° - 74°) = 53°$. But OAC is 17°, so angle $CAB = 53° - 17° = 36°$. 2 marks for the correct answer, otherwise 1 mark for stating or working out OAB correctly.

(d)
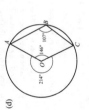

There's an easy way to work it out — but most people don't know it. An angle like ABC is always twice the *outside* angle at the centre (the outside angle at AOC is $360° - 146° = 214°$, so halve this to get $ABC = 107°$).
Here's a harder way to work it out. $COB = COA - AOB = 146° - 74° = 72°$. That means $OBC = (180° - 72°) \div 2 = 108° \div 2 = 54°$ (since it's a isosceles triangle). And we know ABO is 53° from part (b), so $ABC = ABO + OBC = 53° + 54° = 107°$. 2 marks for the correct answer, otherwise 1 mark for a reasonable answer obtained from a similar method to above.
CIRCLE GEOMETRY — no one told me Maths could be such fun.

10(a)

0.4	head	0.4 head	0.16
		0.6 tail	0.24
0.6	tail	0.4 head	0.24
		0.6 tail	0.36

The probability that it will land on heads twice is $0.4 \times 0.4 = 0.16$.
2 marks for the correct answer, otherwise 1 mark for using 0.4 and for multiplying, but somehow getting the wrong answer.

(b) The probability that it will land on tails is 0.6. So the probability that he gets 1 head and 1 tail is $(0.6 \times 0.4) + (0.4 \times 0.6) = 0.24 + 0.24 = 0.48$ (as it could be heads then tails, or tails then heads).
3 marks for the right answer, otherwise 1 mark for each of the underlined probabilities, or writing $2 \times (0.6 \times 0.4)$.
Got a bad feeling about this? Hmmm... that's PROBABILITY for you.

11 (a)(i) The perimeter is the lengths of all the sides added together. That is $P = 2 \times (2x + 7) + (2 \times 3x) = 4x + 14 + 6x = 10x + 14$.
(ii) The area is $A = (3x) \times (2x + 7) = 3x(2x + 7) = 6x^2 + 21x$. (The underlined answer is okay too — it's equally simplified.)
3 marks for both answers correct, otherwise 1 mark for each correct answer, but lose a mark if either or both aren't in their simplest form.

(b) If $P = 34$, then $10x + 14 = 34$, i.e. $x = 2$. Then put this value of x into the formula for A to find that $A = 6 \times 2^2 + 21 \times 2 = 24 + 42 = 66$, so $A = 66\ cm^2$.
3 marks for the correct answer, otherwise 1 mark for finding correct value of x, and 1 mark for substituting into the formula for A.
It's only ALGEBRA — it won't bite.

12 (a)(i) The median time is **17 seconds**. (The middle value falls in the 17 second category.) 1 mark for the correct answer.

(ii) The range of the times is **4 seconds**. (This is the maximum time minus the minimum time.) 1 mark for the correct answer.

(b) One possible list is: **27, 28, 29, 31, 32, 33, 39**. (Then the median is 31 seconds, i.e. the value in the middle is 31, and the difference between the biggest and the smallest is 12 seconds.)
2 marks available — 1 if your list has a median of 31 seconds, and 1 if your list has a range of 12 seconds.
You'd better get this STATISTICS stuff learned — it ain't hard... just boring.

13(a) $u + v = (2+\sqrt{5}) + (2-\sqrt{5}) = 4$. This is **rational**. 1 mark only for both parts of the answer correct ('4' and 'rational').

(b) $u - v = (2+\sqrt{5}) - (2-\sqrt{5}) = 2\sqrt{5}$. This is **irrational**. 1 mark for each part of the answer.

(c) $uv = (2+\sqrt{5})(2-\sqrt{5}) = 2^2 - \sqrt{5}^2 = 4 - 5 = -1$. This is **rational**. 3 marks for getting both parts of the answer correct, otherwise 1 mark for each part, and 1 mark for using the result $\sqrt{5}^2 = 5$.

14(a) $y = \dfrac{a}{(x+b)^2}$, which means that $(x+b)^2 = \dfrac{a}{y}$. So $x + b = \sqrt{\dfrac{a}{y}}$, and therefore $x = \sqrt{\dfrac{a}{y}} - b$.
3 marks for the correct answer, otherwise 1 mark for each of the underlined intermediate stages.

(b)(i) The correct diagram is **diagram D** — 1 mark available.
(ii) y is never zero (because $a \ne 0$). Put $x = 0$ to discover that the curve meets the y-axis at the point $\left(0, \dfrac{a}{b^2}\right)$.
1 mark for the correct coordinates.
Check out ALGEBRA and GRAPHS.

15 The diagram should look like this: The large circle should have a radius of 6 cm, and the small circle should have radius of 2 cm.

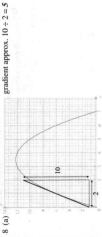

4 marks available — 1 for drawing a circle centred on the airport, 1 for drawing it with a radius of 6 cm; 1 for drawing a circle centred on the square corner of the border, and 1 for giving this a radius of 2 cm. You don't lose any marks for a small mistake with the area shaded, as long as you've got the circles right.
Can't see the point of LOCI? Too bad. They'll still give you a question on it...

16(a) $x^2 + 5x + 6 = (x + 2)(x + 3)$. 2 marks — 1 for each factor.

(b) $\dfrac{x+3}{x^2+5x+6} + \dfrac{2}{x+3} = \dfrac{x+3}{(x+2)(x+3)} + \dfrac{2}{x+3} = \dfrac{(x+5)+2(x+2)}{(x+2)(x+3)} = \dfrac{3x+9}{(x+2)(x+3)}$
This equals $\dfrac{3(x+3)}{(x+2)(x+3)} = \dfrac{3}{x+2}$.
4 marks for the correct answer, otherwise 1 mark for each underlined stage.
Sing along: ALGEBRA is sacred. ALGEBRA is great. If an X is wasted...

17(a)
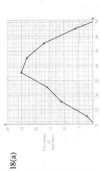

1 mark for entering 5/12 as the probability of getting a red tie, and 1 mark for entering 7/12 as the probability of getting a blue tie. (Get the marks for entering these values at least once.)

(b)(i) The probability that both ties will be blue is $\dfrac{7}{12} \times \dfrac{7}{12} = \dfrac{49}{144}$ (= 0.340).
2 marks for the correct answer (as either fraction or decimal), otherwise 1 mark for multiplying any two probabilities together.
(ii) The probability of the ties being different colours is
$\left(\dfrac{5}{12} \times \dfrac{7}{12}\right) + \left(\dfrac{7}{12} \times \dfrac{5}{12}\right) = 2 \times \dfrac{35}{144} = \dfrac{35}{72}$ (=0.486).
3 marks for the correct answer (as either fraction or decimal), otherwise 1 mark for multiplying two probabilities together.
Get 1 mark for $\dfrac{35}{144}$.
TREE DIAGRAMS — joy of joys.

18(a)

When you plot the frequency polygon, you need to use the points 5.5, 15.5, 25.5 etc. on the horizontal axis, as these are the true mid-class intervals, i.e. halfway between 1 and 10, 11 and 20 etc. 2 marks available — 1 for plotting at least 4 points at the correct place on the horizontal axis, and 1 for plotting at least 4 points at the correct place on the vertical axis.

(b) 29% of the customers are 30 years old or less, and 54% are 40 years old or less. This means that the median age (i.e. the age that 50% are younger than and 50% are older than) must lie in the **31-40 age group**.
2 marks for the correct answer, otherwise 1 mark for a correct explanation but wrong answer.
Don't forget to plot the points at the MIDPOINT of the class.

Paper 2A

1 $\left[\left[2-\frac{12}{20}\right)^{4}-3\right]\times100\Rightarrow\left[(1.4)^{4}-3\right]\times100\Rightarrow[0.8416]\times100=\textbf{84.16\%}$

2 marks for the correct answer, otherwise 1 mark for the right method.
If you're a bit rusty, practise your POWERS (or INDICES).

2 Time on watch = 55 seconds. Average speed given by $\frac{\text{total distance}}{\text{total time}}$.

Now, distance = 0.4 km = $\frac{4}{10}$ km,

and time = 55 secs = $\frac{55}{60\times60}=\frac{55}{3600}$ hrs.

So speed = $\frac{\text{distance}}{\text{time}}=\frac{\frac{4}{10}}{\frac{55}{3600}}=\frac{4\times3600}{10\times55}=\frac{4\times72}{11}=\frac{288}{11}$ km/h = **26.2 km/h**

3 marks for the correct answer, otherwise 1 mark for converting the units correctly, and 1 quoting the formula for speed correctly. *SPEED, DISTANCE AND TIME and CONVERSION FACTORS. Lovely question.*

3 (a) $p+q=(4+\sqrt5)+(4-\sqrt5)=4+\sqrt5+4-\sqrt5=\textbf{8}$ — *RATIONAL*

1 mark for the right answer.

(b) $p-q=(4+\sqrt5)-(4-\sqrt5)=4+\sqrt5-4+\sqrt5=\textbf{2}\sqrt5$ — *IRRATIONAL*

1 mark for the right answer.

(c) $pq=(4+\sqrt5)(4-\sqrt5)=(4\times4)+(\sqrt5\times\sqrt5)-4\sqrt5+4\sqrt5$
$=16-5=\textbf{11}$ — *RATIONAL*

3 marks for the right answer, otherwise 1 mark for the correct expansion, and 1 if you square $\sqrt5$ correctly.
POWERS AND ROOTS... RATIONAL AND IRRATIONAL NUMBERS... it's all starting to get a bit serious.

4 (a) $105\leqslant$ weight <115 so the minimum weight is **105 g**. (Anything less would be rounded down to 100 g.)

(b) $265-\frac{5}{2}\leqslant$ weight $<265+\frac{5}{2}$, i.e. $262.5\leqslant$ weight <267.5 so if a value is recorded as 265, the highest possible value is **267.5 g** (or 267.499 recurring, which is equivalent). Anything less than this is wrong, as there would always be a larger number that would still be rounded down (even though 267.5 would be rounded up, not down).
It's making you sweat, there's only one thing to do... more ACCURACY AND ESTIMATING.

5 (a) 4 cm increases to 7 cm, so you have to multiply everything by a scale factor of 7/4. So DC becomes $12\times\frac{7}{4}=\textbf{21 cm}$.

2 marks for the correct answer, otherwise 1 mark for the method.

(b) To find the original length, you have to divide by the scale factor.
So $14\div\frac{7}{4}=14\times\frac{4}{7}=\textbf{8 cm}$.

2 marks for the correct answer, otherwise 1 mark for the method.

(c)$70°$ — 1 mark only.

6 $ax-by-ay=a(x-y)+b(x-y)+(-y+x)$.

But this equals $a(x-y)+b(x-y)=\textbf{(a+b)}\,\textbf{(x-y)}$.

Check this multiplies out: $(a+b)(x-y)=ax-ay+bx-by$ ✔

2 marks for the correct answer, otherwise 1 mark for either underlined expression.
ALGEBRA. Just take your time and check each step of your working.

7 (a) $a=\frac{v^2-u^2}{2s}=\frac{28^2-42.5^2}{2\times47}=\frac{784-1806.25}{94}=-10.875\Rightarrow\textbf{-10.9}$

Don't worry about the minus sign — that just means it's slowing down rather than speeding up.   1 mark for the correct answer.

(b) $a=\frac{v^2-u^2}{2s}\Rightarrow 2as=v^2-u^2\Rightarrow 2as+u^2=v^2\Rightarrow u^2=v^2-2as\Rightarrow u=\sqrt{v^2-2as}$

2 marks for the correct answer, otherwise 1 mark for either of the intermediate equations above.
You don't even need to know about SPEED, DISTANCE AND TIME for this question — it's just ALGEBRA.

8

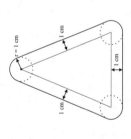

3 marks for the correct answer, otherwise 1 mark for the straight lines 1 cm from the edges of the triangle, and 1 for circular arcs with a radius of 1 cm at the vertices.
More LOCI AND CONSTRUCTIONS...

9 (a) $1.6\times10^7+8.21\times10^{10}=0.0016\times10^{10}+8.21\times10^{10}=\textbf{8.2116}\times\textbf{10}^{\textbf{10}}\ \textbf{m}^2$

2 marks for the correct answer, otherwise 1 for putting both numbers into the same order of magnitude (i.e. making them both $\times10^{10}$). *STANDARD INDEX FORM again. No rest for the wicked.*

(b) The ratio is $1.6\times10^7:8.21\times10^{10}$. But you need it in the ratio 1 : n, so divide both sides by 1.6×10^7, to get

$\text{ratio}=1:\frac{8.21\times10^{10}}{1.6\times10^7}=\frac{8.21\times10^{10-7}}{1.6}=1:5.13125\times10^3=\textbf{1:5131.25}$

2 marks for the correct answer, otherwise 1 for any of the underlined formulas.
SIMILARITY AND ENLARGEMENTS — easy when you know how.

10(a)(i) Put $y=0$ into both equations to find the coordinates of C and D, then D is the one with the larger x-coordinate:

$4x+3y=21\Rightarrow 4x=21\Rightarrow x=\frac{21}{4}=5.25$

$3x+4y=21\Rightarrow 3x=21\Rightarrow x=\frac{21}{3}=7$

7 is the larger x-coordinate, so the second equation is that of the line AD.

$\therefore AD$ is $\textbf{3x+4y=21}$ Alternatively, you could do the same thing for the y-coordinates: look at $x=0$ and take the one with the lower y coordinate. Or you could work out the gradients of both lines and take the line with the higher gradient (bearing in mind that they're both negative). But I wouldn't recommend that approach — it's a lot more hassle.

A measly 1 mark for the correct answer.

(ii) To find the y coordinate of A, put $x=0$ into $3x+4y=21$
$\Rightarrow 4y=21\Rightarrow y=\frac{21}{4}$, so the coordinates of A are $\left(\textbf{0,}\frac{\textbf{21}}{\textbf{4}}\right)$

To find the x coordinate of C, put $y=0$ in $4x+3y=21$
$\Rightarrow 4x=21\Rightarrow x=\frac{21}{4}$, so the coordinates of C are $\left(\frac{\textbf{21}}{\textbf{4}}\textbf{,0}\right)$

2 marks available — 1 mark for each pair of coordinates correct.

(b)

Area of $OABC$ = {2 ×(area of triangle)} + area of square
$=\{2\times(\frac12\times2\sqrt4\times3)\}+(3\times3)$
$=(2\sqrt4\times3)+9=\textbf{15\sqrt4 units}^2$

5 marks for correct answer, otherwise 2 marks for dividing it up into shapes that are easy to calculate, 1 mark for working out area of square, and 1 mark for area of either one or both shaded triangles.

11(a)(i)95 = 21 × 5 = **19 × 5**   2 marks available — 1 for each prime factor.

(ii)   105 = 21 × 5 = 7 × 3 × 5   2 marks for the correct answer, otherwise 1 mark for breaking 105 down into prime factors (e.g. 21 × 5, or 35 × 3).

(b) The lowest common multiple (LCM) of 95 and 105 is 19 × 5 × 7 × 3 = 1995, so after 1995 s both motorbikes will be back on the starting line. This is 1995 ÷ 60 = 33.25 minutes = **33 mins 15 s**.

3 marks available for the right answer, otherwise 1 mark for finding the LCM and 1 mark for the underlined answer.
Prime number problems? Revise PRIME NUMBERS. Well what did you think I was going to say...

12 Trial and improvement — so guess your first number...
Using $x=3$ gives $3^3+3=27+3=30$. This is too small, so try $x=4$, which gives $4^3+4=64+4=68$. This is too big, so the answer is somewhere between 3 and 4. Try $x=3.5$.

$x=3.5$ giving $3.5^3+3.5=46.375$. This is just too big, so try
$x=3.4$ giving $3.4^3+3.4=42.704$

Your answer only needs to be to 1 d.p. so 3.4 is likely to be the answer you're looking for. Check this by using $x=3.45$ in the equation —
$3.45^3+3.45=44.514$ — it's too large, so $3.4<x<3.45$ and the answer to 1 d.p. is **3.4.**

4 marks available — 1 for using a trial and improvement method, 1 for at least two correct calculations, 1 for at least one correct response to an answer which is too large or too small (i.e. trying something bigger or smaller as necessary), and 1 for the final answer.

13 (a)   Min. length of 376 biscuits $=376\times(69-1.5)$
$=376\times67.5=25380$ nm $=\textbf{25.38 m}$

3 marks for the correct answer, otherwise 1 for correct minimum diameter of a biscuit and 1 for multiplying this by 376. Lose a mark if you left your answer in millimetres.

(b) Volume of 1 biscuit $=\pi r^2\times\text{thickness}$, so the maximum possible volume of 1 biscuit is given by

$\pi\left(\frac{d_{max}}{2}\right)^2\times\text{maximum thickness}$ (since radius $=\frac12\times$diameter)

(where d_{max} is the maximum possible diameter of a biscuit)

$=\pi\times\left(\frac{(69+1.5)}{2}\right)^2\times(7.9+0.5)$

$=\pi\times35.25^2\times8.4$ $=\textbf{32790 mm}^3$ (or 32795 mm³ if you take π as 3.142)
$=\textbf{3.28}\times\textbf{10}^{\textbf{4}}\ \textbf{mm}^3$

3 marks — 1 for the correct formula for the volume, 1 for a correct value of either the maximum radius / diameter or the maximum thickness, and 1 for the final answer.

14(a) $y=6\times4^{-\frac{t}{4}}$. Initially $t=0$, so $y=6\times4^0=6\times1=\textbf{6 mg}$.

1 mark for the correct answer.
Trouble with your ROOTS? Get yourself to the hairdressers...

(b)

Time after injection (t minutes)	5	10	15	20	25	30	35
Amount of sedative remaining (y mg)	3.89	2.52	1.64	1.06	0.69	0.45	0.29

4 marks to get here — 1 for at least 1 correct value, 2 for 2 correct, 3 for 3 correct and 4 for at least 5 correct.
Having trouble getting your calculator to do what you want? See CALCULATOR BUTTONS.

(c)

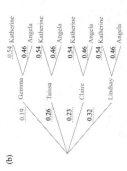

3 marks for an accurate graph, with all points correct. 2 marks for at least 4 points correct, otherwise no marks. Lose a mark if the line isn't drawn accurately — it should be a smooth curve that passes as near to each point as possible. (You get the marks for plotting your answers to part (b) correctly, even if you got part (b) wrong.)
It's just a TYPICAL GRAPH QUESTION.

15(a)P(G or L) = 0.19 + 0.32 = **0.51**   1 mark for the correct answer.

(b)

Gemma — 0.54 Katherine
— 0.46 Angela
Taissa — 0.54 Katherine
0.26 — 0.46 Angela
Claire — 0.54 Katherine
0.23 — 0.46 Angela
Lindsay — 0.54 Katherine
0.32 — 0.46 Angela
0.19 —

2 marks available — 1 for getting the probability of Angela winning right, and the other for putting all the probabilities in the correct places.

(c) Use tree diagram — P(T and A) = 0.26 × 0.46 = 0.1196 = **0.12**

2 marks for the correct answer, otherwise 1 mark for multiplying two probabilities together — even if they're the wrong ones.
Find out more in next week's exciting episode of... PROBABILITY.

16 (a)

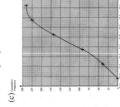

Frequency Density axis: 4.0, 3.5, 3.0, 2.5, 2.0, 1.5, 1.0, 0.5, 0.0
Age in years: 0 10 20 30 40 50 60 70

The thing with a histogram is you plot the frequency densities, not the frequencies.
So you've got to divide each frequency by the age range it covers — so you get:

For $15 \le y < 20$, $4 \div 5 = 0.8$ For $20 \le y < 25$, $9 \div 5 = 1.8$

For $25 \le y < 30$, $18 \div 5 = 3.6$ For $30 \le y < 40$, $12 \div 10 = 1.2$

For $40 \le y < 50$, $32 \div 10 = 3.2$ For $50 \le y < 70$, $25 \div 20 = 1.25$

(If you didn't do it that way, the area of each bar wouldn't be proportional to the frequency, so it would be misleading.)
4 marks available — 2 marks for plotting frequency densities rather than frequencies (or 1 mark if they've been worked out wrong), and 2 marks for plotting all the bars accurately (whether or not frequency densities have been plotted), or 1 mark if at least 3 bars are accurate.
This stuff is all covered in SCATTER GRAPHS AND HISTOGRAMS.

(b) Take the mid-class values to find the average age now:

$$\Rightarrow \frac{(4\times17.5)+(9\times22.5)+(18\times27.5)+(12\times35)+(32\times45)+(25\times60)}{4+9+18+12+32+25}$$

$$= \frac{70+202.5+495+420+1440+1500}{100} = \frac{4127.5}{100} = 41.3 \text{ (to 1 d.p.)}$$

In 3 years' time the average age will have increased by 3 years, so the average age will be $41.3 + 3 =$ **44.3 years.**
4 marks available — 1 mark for the idea of using mid-class values to calculate the mean, 1 for getting the correct current mean age, and 1 for adding 3 on to find the average age in 3 years. (Or for adding 3 to each mid-class interval at the start.)
GROUPED FREQUENCY TABLES — bit tricky, aren't they...

(c) Histogram likely to be roughly the same shape. (even exactly the same). It's likely that some members will now be in the next higher age range, so some bars could be lower, some higher. If anyone was at least 67 at the time of the 1st histogram, they wouldn't appear on the 2nd one, so total area would be less — but otherwise total area would be unchanged (or total of heights if you didn't plot frequency densities). First bar couldn't be any higher, but might be lower.
2 marks for any two of the above points, or 1 mark for one of the points.
Yup — it's HISTOGRAMS again...

17

Original population density $= \dfrac{92000}{118} = 779.67$ people / square km (to 2 d.p.)

New pop. dens. $= \dfrac{92000+14000}{118+7} = \dfrac{106000}{125} = 848$ people/km².

So the population density will be increased by
$848 - 779.66 =$ **68.34 people / square km.**
4 marks available, otherwise 1 mark for correct <u>original</u> population density, 1 for correct <u>new</u> pop. dens., and 1 mark for correct subtraction.

18 (a)

$x^2 - 6x - 5 = (x-a)^2 - b = x^2 - 2ax + (a^2 - b)$
So $2a = 6 \Rightarrow a = 3$
Therefore $x^2 - 6x - 5 = (x-3)^2 - b = x^2 - 6x + (9 - b)$
And so $9 - b = -5 \Rightarrow b = 14$ So the answer is $(x-3)^2 - 14$
2 marks available — 1 for the correct value of a, and 1 for b.

(b) $x^2 - 6x - 5 = 0 \Rightarrow (x-3)^2 - 14 = 0 \Rightarrow (x-3)^2 = 14 \Rightarrow x-3 = \pm\sqrt{14}$
$\Rightarrow x = 3 \pm \sqrt{14} =$ **−0.74, or 6.74**
3 marks for both correct answers, otherwise 1 mark for the method above (or for sustituting the right values into the quadratic formula), and 1 mark for getting either of the values for x correct.
COMPLETING THE SQUARE — innit great...

19 (a)

The modal group is the one with the highest frequency, so this must be **24.6 − 24.8 mm.** — 1 mark for correct answer.

(b)

Length (mm)	Frequency	Cumulative frequency
24.0 - 24.2	39	39
24.3 - 24.5	53	92
24.6 - 24.8	76	168
24.9 - 25.1	57	225
25.2 - 25.4	15	240

(c)

3 marks available — 1 for getting at least 3 of these correct (still get the mark if you get an early entry wrong but use the correct method to find the next one — you just have to use the correct method at least 3 times).

3 marks available — 1 for getting at least 3 upper class values correct (values on length axis — **23.95, 24.25, 24.55, 24.85, 25.15 and 25.45**), 1 for plotting at least 2 points correctly and 1 for drawing the curve correctly.
Check out CUMULATIVE FREQUENCY if you're stumped.

(d)

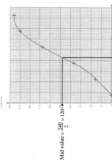

Mid value $= \dfrac{240}{2} = 120$

Mean value $= 24.65$

1 mark for any answer between 23.8 and 25.2, and 1 mark for saying that you need to find the value of the curve when the cumulative frequency is 120 (half the total frequency).

20 (a)

If he uses all his fencing, $AB + BC + CD = 80$, but $AB = CD = x$, so this becomes $2x + BC = 80$, i.e. $BC = 80 - 2x$.

So the area of the pen $= AB \times BC = x(80 - 2x) = 80x - 2x^2$
$\Rightarrow 80x - 2x^2 = 500 \Rightarrow 2x^2 - 80x + 500 = 0 \Rightarrow x^2 - 40x + 250 = 0$
3 marks available — 1 for substituting x for AB and $(80-2x)$ for BC, 1 for equating this to the total area (500), and 1 for the correct working to get the equation in the form asked for.
You need to know your ALGEBRA and AREAS for this one.

(b) It's a bit tricky, so use the quadratic formula. If $ax^2 + bx + c = 0$, then
$$x = \frac{-b\pm\sqrt{b^2-4ac}}{2a} = \frac{40\pm\sqrt{(-40)^2-(4\times1\times250)}}{2} = \frac{40\pm\sqrt{1600-1000}}{2} = 20 \pm \frac{\sqrt{600}}{2} = 20 \pm \sqrt{150} = 32.25 \text{ or } 7.75$$

So $x =$ **32.25 m or 7.75 m.**
3 marks for both correct answers, otherwise 1 mark for the formula, or complete the square if you're feeling brave), and 1 mark for one of the answers right. Also, lose a mark for not quoting the answers to either 1 or 2 decimal places.
Check out THE QUADRATIC FORMULA. It's ace.

Paper 2B

1 (a) **5p + 4q**   Perimeter is a length. So find the expressions with length dimensions. Award one mark for correct answer.

(b) **2p(p+q), 2p²/q**   The expressions which could represent an area are those with (length)² dimensions. 2 marks available, one for each correct answer. If more than 2 answers are given, award no marks.

2 (a) **4abi(3a − 2b)**   2 marks for correct answer. Award only 1 mark if 4 has not been taken out as a common factor i.e. abi(12a−8b).

(b)(i) a^7 (Use the power law: $a^m \times a^n = a^{m+n}$)
So just add the powers. $a \times a^6 = a^{1+6} = a^7$.   1 mark for correct answer.

(ii) $9b^6$ Remove the bracket, applying the power everything inside the bracket: $(3b^3)^2 = 3^2 \times b^{3\times2} = 9b^6$. (So you use the power laws $(ba)^n = b^n a^n$ and $(a^n)^m = a^{nm}$) 1 mark for correct answer.

(iii) b^{-3} or $\dfrac{1}{b^3}$ Just subtract the powers, using the power law
$\dfrac{a^m}{a^n} = a^{m-n}$
1 mark for correct answer

(c) (i) $\dfrac{a^{-4}}{9}$ or $\dfrac{1}{9a^4}$ $(3a^2)^{-2} = 3^{-2} \times a^{2\times-2} = \frac{1}{9}a^{-4}$
1 mark for correct answer.

(ii) $\dfrac{6y^6}{x^2}$ $8x^3y^3 \times \dfrac{3y^4}{4x^5} = 6y^{2+4}x^{3-5} = 6y^6x^{-2}$
1 mark for correct answer.

3 **Upper bound — 86.275 (or 86.2749)**
Lower bound — 86.265
86.275 is the upper bound, even though it would be rounded up to 86.28.
If you choose any number lower than this, you could always pick a higher number still lower than 86.275, so it couldn't be the upper bound.
86.265 is the lowest bound because any number lower than that would be rounded down to 86.26 or less.
1 mark available for each correct answer.

4 (a) $x = \dfrac{y}{(6-a)}$ $y = 6x - ax \Rightarrow y = x(6-a) \Rightarrow x = \dfrac{y}{(6-a)}$
2 marks available for the right answer, or 1 mark for using the right method.

(b)(i) $p^2, \dfrac{1}{p}, p^{\frac{1}{2}}, p$.
$\dfrac{1}{p} < 1$ if $p >1$. So $\dfrac{1}{p^2} = \dfrac{1}{p} \times \dfrac{1}{p} < \dfrac{1}{p}$ $p^{\frac{1}{2}} >1$ for $p>1$. But $p^{\frac{1}{2}} < p$.
The easiest way to make sure is to choose a number >1 and try it out. If $p = 2$: $p^2 = 4$, $\dfrac{1}{p} = 0.5$, $\dfrac{1}{p^2} = 0.25$, $\dfrac{1}{p} = \dfrac{1}{2} = 0.5$, $p^{\frac{1}{2}} = \sqrt{2} = 1.414$, $p = 2$.
2 marks for correct answer. Otherwise award 1 mark if good explanation is given and only one is out of place.

(ii) $p, p^{\frac{1}{2}}, \dfrac{1}{p}, p^2$. Order is reversed, because when $0<p<1$, multiplying by p makes a term smaller, not larger. Again, just test it for a particular value:
If $p = \frac{1}{2}$, $p^{\frac{1}{2}} = \sqrt{0.5} = 0.71$, $\dfrac{1}{p} = 2$, $p^2 = 4$.
1 mark for the correct answer.

5 (a)(i) *31.* 15 + 16 = 31. 1 mark available.
(ii) *Double then add 1.* $n + 2^{n-1}$. 1 mark available.
(b) 2 marks for correct answer.

6 (a) $\frac{1}{4}$. 1 out of the 4 shapes is a star. 1 mark available.
(b) $\frac{1}{16}$. $\frac{1}{4} \times \frac{1}{4} = \frac{1}{16}$. 2 marks available for the correct answer, otherwise 1 mark for the right method.
(c) $\frac{3}{4}$. The probability that Paul and Leila will draw the same picture is $\frac{1}{4}$. (There are 16 possible outcomes and 4 of them will be matching. Which means the probability of them drawing the same is $\frac{4}{16} = \frac{1}{4}$.)
The probability that they will draw different pictures is $1 - \frac{1}{4} = \frac{3}{4}$.
3 marks for the correct answer, otherwise 2 marks for a valid method.

7 (a) *AB — Chris walked away from his home at a constant speed for 9 km over 1½ hours. BC — Chris' distance from his home didn't change for 1½ hours (he could have been stationary). CD — Chris walks back 5 km towards his home at a constant speed for ½ hour.* This TRAVEL GRAPHS stuff's pretty easy really — just get a bit of practice in.
(b) *CD.* The gradient is steepest. 1 mark available.
(c) *3 km/h* - Imagine a straight line from A to C, just work out the the gradient of this straight line. Gradient = $(9-0) \div (3-0) = 3$.
2 marks for correct answer, 1 mark for correct method (i.e. finding gradient or for correctly using the formula SPEED = DISTANCE / TIME)

8 (a) $(5x+3)(2x-4) = 10x^2 - 20x + 6x - 12 = 10x^2 - 14x - 12$.
2 marks available.
(b)(i) $(2x-1)(x+5)$. $2x^2 + 9x - 5 = (2x-1)(x+5)$. 1 mark available for the correct answer.
(ii) $x = \frac{1}{2}$, or -5. Use the factorised equation from the previous question. 2 marks available for the right answer, or 1 mark for the right method.

9 $x = 5$, $y = 2$. Label the equations A $(3x + 4y = 23)$ and B $(2x - 2y = 6)$. Multiply B by 2 to get equation Bi: Add A and Bi together to get $7x = 35$, so $x = 5$. Put this back into one of the equations to find y: $3x + 4y = 23 \Rightarrow 15 + 4y = 23 \Rightarrow 4y = 8 \Rightarrow y = 2$. 4 marks available for the correct answer, or one mark for each underlined method used correctly.

10 $a = 3$, $b = -45$. Find 2 points on the line, (x_1, y_1) and (x_2, y_2).
Then find $\frac{(y_2 - y_1)}{(x_2 - x_1)}$, to give you the gradient = a.
e.g. $\frac{(15-0)}{(20-15)} = \frac{15}{5} = 3$.
3 marks available for the correct answer, or 2 marks for the right method.

11 $x > 2$. $x^2 - 4x + 8 > (x-4)^2 \Rightarrow x^2 - 4x + 8 > x^2 - 8x + 16$
$\Rightarrow -4x + 8 > -8x + 16 \Rightarrow 4x > 8 \Rightarrow x > 2$. 3 marks available for the right answer, or 2 marks for using the right method but getting the answer wrong.

12(a) *£550.* 10% = 0.1. £500 × 1.1 = £550. 1 mark available.
(b) *£605.* £550 × 1.1 = £605. 2 marks available.
(c) *£665.50.* £605 × 1.1 = £665.50. 2 marks available.

---

13 *7.5 cm.* ½(3.5 + 6.5) × 1.5 = ½ × 10 × 1.5 = 7.5 cm
3 marks available for the right answer, or 2 marks for the right method.

14(a) *B.* 1 mark available.
(b) *A.* 1 mark available.
(c) *C.* 1 mark available.
(d) *D.* 1 mark available.

15(a)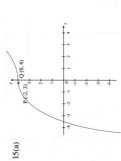
P is now (-2, 3) and Q is (0, 4).
3 marks available: 1 mark for drawing the graph correctly, and 1 mark each for P and Q.
(b) *P is now (-2, 0) and Q is (0, 3).*
3 marks available: 1 mark for drawing the graph correctly, and 1 mark each for P and Q.
(c) *P is now (0, 0) and Q is (2, 1).*
3 marks available: 1 mark for drawing the graph correctly, and 1 mark each for P and Q.

16 (a) First of all, find an expression for the total length of the edges E m:
E = 2×(3 edges of triangle) + 3×A
= 2(5x+5x+6x) + 3A = 32x + 3A
So just rearrange this to make A the subject:
3A = E − 32x → A = $\frac{1}{3}$(E − 32x)
2 marks available. Award 1 mark for writing down the expression for E correctly in terms of A. Award the other mark for correctly rearranging the formula to make A the subject.

(b) Surface area S = (Area of the triangle × 2) + area of the 3 rectangles
To find the area of the triangle, you need to use pythagoras's theorem on one of the right-angled triangles made by splitting the triangle vertically into two.
Height of triangle = $\sqrt{25x^2 - 9x^2} = \sqrt{16x^2} = 4x$
$25x^2 - 9x^2$ = Area of triangle = ½ × base × height = ½ × 6x ×4x = $12x^2$
So S = $(12x^2 × 2) + 5xA + 5xA + 6xA = 24x^2 + 16Ax$
3 marks available. Award 1 mark for the top line. Award 1 mark for finding the area of the triangle. Award full marks for showing the full method and arriving at the correct answer.

(c) *x = 2 m*
First of all, write down an expression for the volume V.
V = area of triangle × A = $12x^2A$
Now substitute in the values given for A and V:
$240 = 12x^2 × 5$.
Rearrange and solve for x:
$240 = 60x^2$, so $x^2 = 4$, so $x = 2$ m.

17(a) *22°* The triangles AOP and BOP are congruent, because the two tangents from a point to a circle are always equal. So OPA = OPB = 22°.
(b) *68°* The angle that the tangent makes with the radius OB is 90°. So POB = 180° − 90° − 22° = 68°. This is a property of tangents.
(c) *124°* ODB is isosceles (since two of its sides are radii). So angle ODB = (180 − 68)÷2 = 56°. So angle BDP = 180° − 56° = 124° (since they lie on a straight line).
d) Angle AOD = DOB = 68° by symmetry. So ACB = 2 × 68 = 136°. Now ACB = ½AOB (using the circle property that says the angle made at the centre of the circle from 2 points is double the angle made at a point on the edge of circle).
So angle ACB = ½ × 136 = 68°.

18 (a)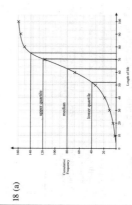
(b) *20 bulbs.*
Draw a vertical line up from 75 hours and read across horizontally to find the cumulative frequency at this point. You should get 140. This is the estimated number of bulbs which lasted up to 75 hours. But you want the number which lasted longer. So it's 160 − 40 = 20 bulbs.
(c)(i) *63 hours*
To find the median, you need to find the estimated length of life of the bulb in the middle. Draw a horizontal line across at the cumulative frequency at the point 80.5 (½×(160 +1)). And read the value this gives for the length of life. You should get 63 hours.
1 mark available. Award the mark for answer between 62 and 64 hours inclusive.

(ii) *18 hours*
To find the interquartile range draw horizontal lines at the points 40 and 120 to find the values of the lower and upper quartiles respectively. (Strictly it would be 40.5 and 120.5.) You should get 52 for the lower quartile and 70 for the upper quartile. This gives an interquartile range of 70 − 52 = 18 hours.
3 marks available. Award full marks for answers between 17 and 19 inclusive. If answer is outside acceptable range, award 1 mark for finding the upper and lower quartiles using the correct method. And award another mark for using these values to find an interquartile range value.

(d) *Less reliable* — If the median were 63 (i.e. the same), but the interquartile range were 24 (i.e. larger), you would expect the bulbs to be less reliable as this indicates that their life lengths were more spread rather than concentrated around the median.
1 mark for correct answer with similar explanation.

19(a)(i) Answer is $a - \frac{b}{2}$.
From the diagram, $\overrightarrow{PD} = \overrightarrow{PA} + \overrightarrow{AD}$.
But $\overrightarrow{PA} = \frac{-\overrightarrow{AB}}{2} = -\frac{b}{2}$. So $\overrightarrow{PD} = -\frac{b}{2} + a = a - \frac{b}{2}$.
Award 1 mark for correct answer.
(ii) Answer is $\frac{2}{3}(-a + b)$
$\overrightarrow{DQ} = \frac{2}{3}\overrightarrow{DB}$. Now $\overrightarrow{DB} = -a + b$, so $\overrightarrow{DQ} = \frac{2}{3}(-a+b)$.
Award 1 mark for correct answer.
(b)(i) Answer is $\frac{1}{2}b + a$
$\overrightarrow{PC} = \overrightarrow{PB} + \overrightarrow{BC}$. Award 1 mark for correct answer.
(ii) Answer is $\frac{1}{3}(\frac{1}{2}b + a) = \frac{1}{3}a + \frac{1}{6}b$
$\overrightarrow{PQ} = \overrightarrow{PB} + \overrightarrow{BQ}$. So you need to find $\overrightarrow{BQ}$:
$\overrightarrow{QB} = \frac{1}{3}\overrightarrow{DB}$ (because $\overrightarrow{DQ} = \frac{2}{3}\overrightarrow{DB}$ and $\overrightarrow{DQ} + \overrightarrow{QB} = \overrightarrow{DB}$)
So $\overrightarrow{BQ} = -\frac{1}{3}\overrightarrow{DB} = -\frac{1}{3}(-a+b) = \frac{1}{3}(a-b)$.
$\overrightarrow{PQ} = \frac{b}{2} + \overrightarrow{BQ} = \frac{b}{2} + \frac{1}{3}(a - b) = \frac{b}{6} + \frac{1}{3}a$
2 marks for the correct answer. Otherwise award 1 mark if you get the method right i.e. if you use $\overrightarrow{PQ} = \overrightarrow{PB} + \overrightarrow{BQ}$ and find expressions for $\overrightarrow{PB}$ and $\overrightarrow{BQ}$.

(c) *Q lies $\frac{1}{3}$ of the way along the line PC.*
We've found that $\overrightarrow{PC} = \frac{1}{2}b + a$ and $\overrightarrow{PQ} = \frac{1}{3}(\frac{1}{2}b + a)$. So these vectors are proportional — and this means Q lies on the line PC and is actually $\frac{1}{3}$ of the way along it. 2 marks available. Award full marks for saying that Q is on the line PC. Or award only 1 mark for saying that the vectors are proportional or something equivalent to this.